Connect to
NCTM Standards 2000

Making the Standards
Work at Grade 2

Francis (Skip) Fennell, Ph.D.

Honi J. Bamberger, Ph.D.

Thomas E. Rowan, Ph.D.

Kay B. Sammons

Anna R. Suarez

Creative Publications
A Tribune Education Company

Acknowledgments

Project Editors → Diane Nieker, Jeff Stiegel

Writers → Tim Burnett, Marilyn Davis, Beth Sycamore

Writing and Editorial Services → MathLink, Inc.

Design Director → Karen Stack

Design → Gerta Sorensen-London

Project Coordinator → Barbara Quincer

Cover Illustration → Jim Dandy

Illustrators → Susan Aiello, Jim Dandy, Sarah Frederking

Production → Inkwell Publishing Solutions, Inc

Manufacturing → Dallas Richards

© 2000 Creative Publications®, Inc.

Two Prudential Plaza

Chicago, IL 60601

This is an independent publication and is not affiliated with, or sponsored by, the NCTM. The NCTM 2000 Standards are not reproduced in this book. This book is designed to be read independently of the *Principles and Standards for School Mathematics* and to aid educators in preparing to teach in a manner consistent with the *Principles and Standards.*

ISBN 0-7622-1244-6

Catalog No. 21208

Customer Service 800-624-0822

http://www.creativepublications.com

1 2 3 4 5 6 7 8 MAL 05 04 03 02 01 00

Contents

Overview

Since *Curriculum and Evaluation Standards for School Mathematics* was released in 1989, much has been learned about how ideas work in the classroom and how children learn mathematics. The release of the *Principles and Standards for School Mathematics* creates an opportunity for us to examine our goals, our math curricula, and our teaching methods in light of these new insights and to consider practices and procedures that will improve school mathematics education. As did the original draft, *Principles and Standards* promotes ways for all educators to strengthen the teaching and learning of mathematics by addressing two important concerns: the characteristics of instructional programs that will provide high-quality mathematical experiences for children as they progress through school, and the mathematical content and processes children should know and use as they advance from grade to grade.

General Overview

Connect to NCTM Standards 2000 is designed to help you understand and implement the NCTM standards. Regardless of your teaching style, the information presented in this book will help you to make the standards work. *Principles and Standards* identifies ten standards. Five of those standards are described as content standards that organize all of mathematics into five broad areas of learning; they address *what* children learn. The other five standards, the process standards, are concerned with *how* children learn and how information is presented.

Today, more than ever, there is a need for all children to have a strong base in mathematics. This means that children do not just memorize facts and procedures, but that they have an understanding of mathematics and mathematical thinking. The interplay between content and process is complicated, but integrating the two is critical if our children are to receive the mathematics education they will need to function effectively in the world they will grow into.

The lessons contained within *Connect to NCTM Standards 2000* are organized into sections by content. Each section contains four lessons dealing with some aspect of that content standard. Each lesson demonstrates ways to develop the content by using the process standards. An overview highlights grade-level content skills and gives a brief description of the four lessons for that standard.

Content Standards

Number and Operation

Algebra

Geometry

Measurement

Data Analysis and Probability

Process Standards

Problem Solving

Reasoning and Proof

Communication

Connections

Representation

The last section of the book, entitled Create Your Own Lesson, is designed to help you develop lessons of your own that will comfortably incorporate the NCTM standards with your teaching style.

About the Lessons

Each content standard section contains four lessons that address some aspect of the content at the grade level. Three of the lessons have been specially developed to model ways the process standards can be used to develop the content being presented. The fourth lesson examines a hypothetical math textbook lesson in terms of how the process standards are incorporated into that lesson. Suggestions are offered for increasing the focus on three of the five process standards to create a more effective lesson. Then, a lesson is presented modeling how those suggestions can be implemented.

As you read through the lessons, keep in mind that what is offered is only one possible approach. You might have a completely different idea about how to develop the concept, and that's fine. These lessons are intended to provide examples of how the process standards can work to make mathematics lessons more meaningful, and to model questions and techniques that you might incorporate into your teaching. As you read through the lessons, pay attention to how the process standards are being used. Use the ideas presented as a springboard for your own ideas.

Each lesson is intended for a single class period. Some introduce a concept, others require that children have some experience with the concept, and still others are meant to be used at the end of a unit. As you examine these lessons, think about how and where they fit into your curriculum. Any of the lessons here can be used as a replacement for the comparable lesson in your current math program. Try the lessons and see the difference incorporating the process standards can make.

Creating Your Own Lessons

The last section of the book is designed to help you develop lessons of your own that incorporate the NCTM standards and are compatible with your teaching style. You will find questions to help you focus on ideas to consider as you begin to organize a standards-based lesson. You will also have an opportunity to follow the thoughts and decisions one person used in the process of developing a lesson.

About the Authors

Francis (Skip) Fennell, Ph.D.

Dr. Fennell was a member of the writing team of *Principles and Standards for School Mathematics* (NCTM, 2000). He has authored mathematics textbooks, materials for both children and teachers, and numerous articles for leading mathematics journals. Dr. Fennell has served on the Board of Directors of NCTM and as Program Officer of instructional materials and teacher enhancement within the Division of Elementary, Secondary, and Informal Education at the National Science Foundation. He has been selected as Outstanding Mathematics Educator by the Maryland Council of Teachers of Mathematics, and as Professor of the Year by both the Carnegie Foundation and Western Maryland College, where he is a professor of education.

Honi J. Bamberger, Ph.D.

Dr. Bamberger is a recognized math scholar and teacher. She has taught at both the elementary school and college levels, served as an associate research scientist and mathematics consultant for Johns Hopkins University, and contributed as a consultant and content writer for the "Numbers Alive" public television series. Dr. Bamberger has presented her research findings at mathematics conferences across the country, and has been an author for a number of mathematics textbooks. Currently, Dr. Bamberger is executive director of Insight, a consulting firm specializing in professional development in mathematics education.

Thomas E. Rowan, Ph.D.

Dr. Rowan was a member of the working group that wrote the K–4 section of the *Curriculum and Evaluation Standards for School Mathematics*. Since the Standards were first published, he has worked with many school systems to help bring about the transition to standards-based classroom mathematics instruction in grades K–8. Dr. Rowan is a frequent presenter at NCTM and author of mathematics texts and numerous articles on teaching and learning mathematics. He currently teaches at the University of Maryland where he focuses on methods of teaching elementary school mathematics.

Kay B. Sammons

Kay Sammons is currently Elementary Mathematics Supervisor for the Howard County Public Schools in Ellicott City, Maryland, where she is responsible for curriculum and staff development for elementary teachers. She is a frequent presenter at state and national mathematics conferences. In addition to serving as a reviewer for NCTM publications, she has written textbooks and teacher resource materials. Ms. Sammons was honored as Elementary Mathematics Teacher of the Year by the Maryland Council Teachers of Mathematics and as Outstanding Educator of the Year by that same organization.

Anna R. Suarez

Anna Suarez is a national consultant and program director for K–8 Mathematics at the National Science Foundation in Arlington, Virginia. Her participation in an NSF-funded research study, Cognitively Guided Instruction (C.G.I.), helped to develop teachers' knowledge of children's mathematical thinking as the basis for making instructional decisions. She has written staff development materials for both the *Investigations* curriculum and Insight.

About the Standards

The *Principles and Standards for School Mathematics 2000* are built around ten curriculum standards. Five of those standards address the mathematical content, or body of mathematical knowledge, that children should learn. Content standards prescribe *what* is to be taught in mathematics. The content standards are Number and Operation, Algebra, Geometry, Measurement, and Data Analysis and Probability.

The other five standards are process standards. The process standards describe *how* the content is delivered. They address how children will acquire the necessary mathematical content and how that knowledge will be applied. The five process standards are identified as Problem Solving, Reasoning and Proof, Communication, Connections, and Representation.

It should be pointed out that the content standards and process standards are not separate subsets of the whole, but are intricately interrelated. How mathematics is learned is as important as what mathematics is learned. The process standards help to "frame" how the content standards are presented.

It is possible to weave the process standards into the teaching of mathematics through a variety of methods. Children can and should be presented with meaningful problems to solve and situations that require them to reason through information to find solutions. They should be asked to defend their solutions and explain their thinking. In presenting a problem to children, connections might be made to a similar problem to build on previous learning. A representative model might be used to enhance children's understanding of a concept. Continuous communication, written and oral, will provide feedback about children's understanding.

For children to become mathematically powerful, it is essential that they be able to use process skills flexibly. They need to practice applying reasoning to solve problems and proving that their solutions are correct. They need to experiment with a variety of representations and have the ability to use them in solving problems and in illustrating their thinking. They should be able to communicate their mathematical thinking and solutions to the teacher and to other children both orally and in writing. Making connections between problems within mathematics is as essential as is making mathematical connections to disciplines outside of mathematics. The importance of how these processes interrelate and work together cannot be overemphasized.

Content Standards

Number and Operation

Algebra

Geometry

Measurement

Data Analysis and Probability

Process Standards

Problem Solving

Reasoning and Proof

Communication

Connections

Representation

Primary Problem Solving

PROBLEM SOLVING IS AT THE HEART of mathematics—it is what mathematicians do. Balance is achieved through the interrelationship of conceptual learning, basic skills, and problem solving. Developing concepts with concrete representations ensures understanding and enables students to create a strong foundation on which to build. Children need basic skills in order to apply and record their understandings with efficiency. But most importantly, they need good problems to solve, problems in which they can apply their conceptual understanding and utilize basic skills.

In its simplest form, problem solving means finding a solution when the answer is not readily apparent. Because problem solving does not always follow a uniform plan, children need to develop persistence to be able to work problems through to the end. Sometimes persistence means changing direction. *Well, we know that way doesn't work. What should we try next? Is there another way we can look at this problem?* Questions that encourage children to look for other options should be an integral part of the discussions that take place in mathematics classes.

Choosing problems that have relevance to children is an important factor in creating enthusiasm for problem solving. Often, the enthusiasm of the teacher translates into a positive disposition toward problem solving for children. If statements like "Now that's an unusual problem. I wonder how we can find the answer," are part of a teacher's repertoire, children get the notion that problem solving is interesting and they are encouraged to use their own resources to find a path to the solution.

Acquiring a variety of strategies to access for problem solving is essential to experiencing success. Having flexibility to solve problems in different ways enables children to get "unstuck" if they reach a "dead end;" it allows them to have other approaches to try. Children should be provided with instruction and practice in using a wide range of strategies that they can then draw upon.

Many young children come to school with an innate understanding of how to solve mathematical problems. The teachers' task is to build on this problem-solving ability by posing challenging problems that are accessible to all children. Fortunately, the primary classroom is full of wonderful problems for young children.

Asking thought-provoking questions to help children begin and sustain the process of solving the problem is another important role of the teacher.

- *How many days are there until Halloween? How can we find out?*
- *If we divide the class into three teams, how many children will be on each team? What can we do that will help us figure this out?*
- *If everyone gets four crackers, how many crackers will we need altogether? If a box contains 24 crackers, will one box be enough? How many boxes will we need?*
- *If we want to extend our pattern, what shape should come next? How can we find out?*

Children should be encouraged to talk with one another and share their thinking with each other as well as the teacher as they solve problems. "Two heads are better than one" is an old saying that has special meaning in the process

of problem solving. As children work together, they are able to come up with many more approaches to a problem than a child working alone would. The teacher should point out differing strategies for the solution of a problem. Children should be asked to compare the strategies to see if there are similarities and note how they differ. Children should also be asked to consider which solutions they think work best for the particular problem and why. This opens the door to a rich discussion that will broaden the learning experience for all.

Primary Reasoning and Proof

REASONING IS FUNDAMENTAL TO THE STUDY of mathematics— it is a state of mind that causes children to explore, to justify, and to validate. It permeates all content areas and all grade levels. Children are reasoning when they interpret data, when they solve problems, and when they view geometric patterns and shapes. As they are presented with new problems, they use reasoning skills to apply previously acquired information and to test the validity of their solutions. Reasoning is the process by which children make sense of mathematics.

As they develop mathematically, children learn that mathematics is a discipline based on an inherent set of rules. Reasoning begins with intuition. This

intuition is used by even the youngest children in their efforts to make sense of mathematics, and it should be encouraged as the basis of reasoning at all grade levels. This informal intuition will become the basis for reasoning through representations that are more formal and for proofs based upon the rules.

Activities that have children compare, sort, and classify provide wonderful opportunities to develop reasoning skills. In a kindergarten classroom, children might use the buttons in a button jar and sort them by a variety of attributes. One child might place all the buttons of one color together; another might sort the buttons by the number of holes; still another by the material from which they're made, such as metal, plastic, or wood. The reasoning at this age is generally limited to one attribute. But as a child advances to first and second grade, he may be able to sort the buttons by two attributes to make a set that includes only buttons that are red and have four holes. When children explain their rules for sorting and how their choices were made, they are able to validate their thinking.

Being able to identify patterns is another prerequisite for the development of reasoning skills. A child who can recognize that the pattern is 2 hearts and 3 stars will be able to extend the pattern and to predict what shape will come next.

♥♥★★★♥♥★★★

What are some other ways reasoning and proof can be incorporated into the mathematics class? An excellent way is by asking questions. *How did you get your answer? Tell me how you thought about that? Why does your solution work?* Questions such as these help children learn that it is important to have reasons for what they say. They also help children realize that mathematics makes sense and isn't just a system of rules and procedures to be blindly followed.

Another powerful way to develop reasoning in young children is to engage them in mathematical discussions. Piaget believed that in order for children to develop reasoning, it was imperative to have social interaction. Designating time during the mathematics lesson for discussion about their thinking allows that interaction. In any class, there will be a wide range of reasoning ability; it's helpful for children with less mature reasoning abilities to hear from those with well-developed skills. Mathematical discussions increase a child's repertoire of reasoning skills.

In a first grade class, the teacher might ask children to give the sum of 8 + 7. When called upon, a child responds with the sum and is asked to explain how the sum was found.

- One child might explain that he got the answer by counting on his fingers and demonstrate that by physically counting eight fingers and then adding seven more.

- Another child may draw tally marks on paper to represent 8 and 7 and then show that it is equal to 15 by counting to eight and then counting on from there to fifteen.

- Another child might tell you that she knows 8 + 7 = 15 because she can "take the two out of seven and combine it with the eight to make 10. There is 5 left over so 10 and 5 make fifteen. $8 + 7 = 8 + (2 + 5) = 10 + 5 = 15$."

- Still another student might say, "I know that 7 + 7 = 14 and 1 more is 15."

All of these children are using what they know is true about mathematics and using mathematical reasoning to solve the problem. A child who is still counting on his fingers to get that answer will hear strategies from other children that he can begin to think about and later apply.

Working on reasoning skills and having children offer explanations of their thinking to defend their answers in the primary grades helps lay the foundation for more formal mathematical argumentation in later grades.

Primary Communication

WHETHER BETWEEN TEACHER AND CHILD, between a pair of children, or among groups of children, the communication skills of reading, writing, and listening and speaking provide the means for sharing ideas and promoting mathematical understanding. As children express their ideas through oral and written language, they have an opportunity to clarify their thinking and reinforce their own comprehension of concepts they are working with. By listening to explanations given by their classmates, children are exposed to ideas they may not have thought of. This provides a greater network of connections among ideas and, in turn, enhances learning.

Ample opportunities to discuss mathematical ideas should be provided. One extremely effective technique that was described in the previous section on Reasoning and Proof involves presenting an interesting problem to the class, allowing time to solve the problem, and then asking children to explain how they solved the problem. Providing a forum for a number of different solutions to be presented and defended by children results in rich dialogue.

There is a very high level of mental activity associated with social interaction of this nature. Children who are afforded opportunities to take part in these mathematical conversations on a regular basis learn more effectively how to reason and defend their answers. In the process, they also learn to communicate and to clarify and refine their ideas, which leads to deeper understanding.

Through discussion, children also learn to organize their mathematical thinking in order to communicate their ideas to one another. In their exchange of ideas, children naturally want to have their position make sense. Providing opportunities to present their views allows young children to articulate, clarify, organize, and consolidate their thinking. This communication enables them to reflect on what they know and demonstrate this knowledge to others.

When children are able to articulate their ideas the teacher gains insight into their thinking. For example, one kindergarten child told a teacher that he knew 5 + 2 = 8. Because the child was able to verbalize the idea, the teacher was able to help the child modify the answer by asking him to prove the

answer using objects like Teddy Bear Counters. As the child counted 5 and 2 more, he realized that he only had 7, not 8.

Astounding language development is characteristic of the primary grades. It is important at this level that children begin to understand and use the special language of mathematics. Every opportunity to build conventional mathematical vocabulary should be taken advantage of. For example, during playtime as a child explains a shape to his friend and describes it as "the one with 4 sides," there's an opportunity for the teacher to explain that the shape is a *square*.

Putting ideas on paper also helps young children organize their thinking. The act of writing something down causes students to organize ideas and refine them before committing them to paper. Words, pictures, and numbers are all part of written communication. Journal writing, which can begin in kindergarten, helps children relate what they know about mathematics and can serve as an important tool for teachers as they assess their children's mathematical understanding.

Primary grade children should be provided with opportunities to share their mathematical ideas on a daily basis. This process is essential to internalizing mathematics.

Primary Connections

MAKING CONNECTIONS IN MATHEMATICS is a three-fold process. Connections are made when one mathematical idea is used to build another; they are made among different mathematical ideas and content areas; and they are made between mathematics and contexts outside the field of mathematics.

Because mathematics is an integrated discipline, treating it as a whole body of knowledge and focusing on the connections that occur naturally adds dimension to ideas and concepts. How is counting related to addition, addition to subtraction, addition to multiplication, multiplication to area? A cohesive curriculum that is clearly articulated from pre-kindergarten through the twelfth grade, one that connects the mathematical ideas within each grade as well as the mathematics between grade levels, is critical if those connections are to take place.

Making connections to prior mathematical experiences is vital for the understanding of how mathematical ideas build on one another. Teachers need to know what mathematics children learned previously in order to build on that knowledge. In a given unit of study, attention should be paid to ensure that mathematics concepts build upon one another from day to day in a coherent manner. Teachers should also be aware of what their children will be studying in subsequent grades so they can lay the foundation for obvious connections to further studies.

Mathematics permeates other curriculum areas and it is found in the everyday experience outside of school as well. The use of shapes and patterns is prevalent in art and architecture; measurement skills and classification skills are important in science; measurement skills and knowledge of fractions are utilized in cooking and in building models; and measurement skills, data gathering, and statistics are applied in the social sciences.

Because mathematics is often integrated into other subjects at the primary level, the children do not view it as a separate study. They count the number of boys and girls in attendance at school each day. They look for patterns on the calendar and in the environment. They build with blocks, observing and communicating about the attributes of each. They sort and classify a variety of objects. They plant seeds and measure their growth.

As young children strive to make sense of their world, they naturally make connections to prior experiences. As a pre-schooler counts a group of four juice boxes on the table and says, "One, two, three, four," counting numbers are being connected with objects. The counting may be based on hearing someone else count, or the child may have had previous counting experiences and is able to transfer those experiences to this new situation. Many pre-school children are not able to recite a counting number for each object they point to because they have not yet internalized one-to-one correspondence. They don't yet understand that if they count each object and end up at 4, there are 4 objects in the group. How are such connections made? Repeated experiences in the classroom where children have opportunities to count boys, girls, crayons, blocks, and so on, will ensure those connections over time.

It is important for teachers to be conscious of connections that can be made in mathematics and to weave those connections into daily practice. When children are able to connect mathematical ideas both inside and outside of the classroom, they begin to see mathematics as a cohesive body of knowledge.

Primary Representation

REPRESENTATIONS PROVIDE VEHICLES for expressing and internalizing mathematical thought. They are a critical component in shaping the way children access, understand, express, and utilize mathematical ideas. Representations include physical objects, pictures, and symbols. They also include mental images, words, and ideas.

Representations can be formal or informal. Examples of formal representations are the conventional symbols, graphs, diagrams, and so on traditionally introduced in school mathematics. More informal forms are often invented by children as a way of making sense of mathematical ideas and communicating

those ideas to classmates or the teacher. Children should be allowed to create their own understanding and explanations, and to express relationships before more conventional representations are introduced. Connecting to their invented forms will facilitate a meaningful transition to thinking and communicating in the language of mathematics.

As teachers design lessons, choosing the type of representations they feel will best help children understand a concept becomes an important consideration. What shared mathematical language is needed to effectively communicate ideas? What manipulatives or models will be appropriate? How will children record their understanding of the concept? When is it appropriate to move from physical to symbolic representation?

Consider this problem for kindergarten children.

> **A man went fishing in the morning and caught 3 fish. In the afternoon, he caught 4 more fish. How many did he catch all together?**

A kindergarten child might use counters representing the situation to help make sense of the problem.

The teacher must decide when it's appropriate to move to a more formal representation of the information. By the time that child reaches second grade, there should be no difficulty representing that same problem symbolically.

$$3 + 4 = 7$$

There are multiple representations for any mathematics concept. The greater the number of ways to represent the same idea a child has knowledge of, the greater the flexibility available in solving problems. For example, the number 25 can be thought of as 2 tens and 5 ones; the same as a quarter; halfway between 1 and 50; an odd number; one more than 24; five less than 30; 12 + 13; and so on. A child with access to this variety of representations of 25 is able to choose which version is useful for a particular situation.

One way to successfully build multiple representations for a number with young children is to feature a number each day in the classroom. Begin the math period by presenting a number for the day, such as 18, and ask children to find as many ways as they can to make that number. This activity is one that all children can work on, and it will increase their ability to think flexibly. Here are some names for 18 found by a second grader.

$18 + 0$	$17 + 1$	$9 + 9$
$16 + 2$	9×2	$20 - 2$
$6 + 6 + 6$	$10 + 8$	$22 - 4$
$5 + 5 + 5 + 3$	$10 + 10 - 2$	$9 + 8 + 1$

$$1+1+1+1+1+1+1+1+1+1+1+1+1+1+1+1+1+1$$

To begin with, children record their mathematical ideas in very personal ways. As they continue their mathematical growth, they are introduced to conventional representations. Both forms of representation are powerful tools for understanding and communicating abstract ideas.

Conclusion

The process standards are not an end in, and of, themselves. Rather, they provide the advanced organizers or plan for lessons that present important mathematics content. Seeing connections among mathematical topics enables children to reason and make sense of new ideas and problem-solving situations they encounter. Through the process of communication, children are able to represent these new ideas either formally or informally.

Just as the process standards are interrelated, so are the process and content standards. For true mathematical thinking and learning to occur, both process and content need to be skillfully woven into and through each lesson. That is the goal to work toward.

Standard 1 **Number and Operation**

AT THE SECOND GRADE LEVEL, number and operation includes developing the concept of the magnitude of larger numbers, how to record and write two-digit numbers, and a lot of work with the basic operations addition and subtraction, and some beginning work with multiplication. Our lessons are derived from these important topics, and include a lesson on developing a sense of 100, a lesson on subtracting two-digit numbers, a lesson that develops the concept of multiplication, and a lesson on how to record and write a two-digit number.

Three lessons model how the process standards can be used to teach content. A fourth lesson is a hypothetical textbook lesson that we have revised to be more standards based. These four lessons do not represent the entire curriculum, but rather provide glimpses of how, with a more concentrated effort to incorporate the process standards, better mathematics teaching and learning can be achieved.

One lesson we have chosen develops the concept of the magnitude of 100. Through physical representations, a hundred chart, and much communication, children are provided with many angles from which to better understand how many is 100. This lesson also brings in connections to children's ability to groups objects and to skip count to reach 100.

Another lesson we have chosen focuses on subtracting two-digit numbers with regrouping. Children are often taught this as a mechanical procedure. Driven by the process standards of problem solving and reasoning and proof, this lesson presents children with the challenge of figuring out for themselves how to accomplish the subtraction, and explaining their methods to the others in the class. Children are able to use models or make pictures to develop and support their methods.

A third lesson we have chosen develops the concept of multiplication. This lesson is based on the connections children can make to their knowledge of adding equal-sized groups and repeated addition. Representation and communication are also emphasized here as children use different methods for showing a repeated addition situation and discuss how multiplication emerges from these situations.

The hypothetical textbook lesson we have chosen to revise is one that focuses on the recording of two-digit numbers. A problem-solving approach motivates this lesson that is not often approached this way. Children figure out the most efficient way to group objects so they can be counted, and thus recorded. Representation and communication are also important here as children use objects to group and count, and discuss which system is the most efficient.

Standard 1 Lessons

Learning About 100

Subtracting Two-Digit Numbers

Investigating Multiplication

Recording Two-Digit Numbers

Learning About 100

Introduction

Objective → Children will develop an understanding of the importance of 100 through counting patterns and through applications.

Context → Children have counted quantities to at least 50, have used two-digit numerals in algorithms, and know the number names for large numerals. They will continue using 100 as a benchmark for mental math and estimation.

NCTM Standards Focus

The focus of this lesson is to develop a sense of 100 and the quantity the numeral represents. The lesson first encourages children to develop a tactile and a visual understanding of 100 and then connects this understanding to symbolic representation. By using this process and the following three standards, the lesson gives the children a multi-sensory experience of the quantity rather than a purely symbolic one, which is usually the case.

Connections Children extend their work with counting and with patterning by grouping objects to make counting to 100 easier. They use the hundred chart to look for patterns in two-digit numbers.

Representation Children represent 100 by constructing sets with concrete objects. They also represent 100 symbolically using a hundred chart.

Communication Children work in small groups to count to 100 using concrete materials. They decide together how to count out the items and then share their grouping and counting strategies with the class.

Teaching Plan

Materials → Student pages 22–23; clear container/plastic bag; 110 cubes, pennies, beans, or counters; any physical objects that are available in large quantities

DISTRIBUTE STUDENT PAGE 22. Place 100 cubes in a clear container such as a plastic bag. Then place 10 single cubes next to the bag and show both sets to the children. *How can you use the single cubes to estimate the number of cubes in the container/bag?* Talk about the term "estimate" as a careful or thoughtful guess. Assure the children that when they estimate, their answer does not have to be exact, but can be a number that is "about right." Ask them to write their estimates of how many cubes are in the bag on student page 22. Have children share their estimates and tell how 10 single cubes helped them estimate the larger quantity. To see the range of estimates, write the children's estimates in numerical order on the board or overhead.

NEXT ASK THE CHILDREN TO THINK of different ways of counting the cubes in the bag to determine the exact number of cubes. Have them write down the different ways on student page 22 and tell which way they think is best and why.

When children have finished writing down their suggestions, have volunteers share their responses. The children might suggest counting the cubes by 1s, 2s, 5s, or 10s. Try out the different ways with the whole class and discuss the advantages and disadvantages of each count. Children should discover that counting to 100 by 1s takes a long time and that it is easy to lose the count if interrupted. Counting by 2s is somewhat easier and faster, but it is still possible to lose count. Encourage children to group by as large a number as possible and then skip-count the total. Using the cubes in the bag, ask volunteers to demonstrate that counting by 5s or 10s is the easiest and fastest way to count a large number of items.

HAVE CHILDREN COMPARE their estimates to the exact number. Then ask each child to write down how close his/her estimate was to the actual number of cubes in the bag. Then hold a brief class discussion about the closest estimates.

What Might Happen . . . What to Do

Sometimes children might not understand what to do when they are asked to skip-count by a given number. Remind them that skip-counting means counting by 2s, 5s, 10s, etc. Model skip-counting by 2s by saying *2, 4, 6, 8, 10*. Repeat as necessary with groups of 5 and 10. Encourage children to become more fluent in their counting strategies.

CHILDREN NEED MANY EXPERIENCES with grouping, counting, and representing 100. Continue the lesson by having children work in pairs or small groups. Tell them to choose objects in the classroom like beans, counters, cubes, or pennies. Give children student page 23 and ask them to count the objects by 2s, 5s, and 10s. Tell them to record their skip-counting by coloring the numbers they say on the hundred chart. They should use a different color for each different way of counting.

As you listen and ask questions of the children, assess if they can predict which number on the hundred chart they will color next. Encourage them to volunteer that the colored squares form a pattern and to explain how they can use this information. Have children describe and compare the patterns they create on the chart. If necessary, prompt children to point out the following during the discussion.

- Counting by 2s generates 5 columns on the hundred chart. All of the numbers are even.

- Counting by 5s generates 2 columns. All of the numbers in one column end in 5 and in the other column in 0.

- Counting by 10s generates one column on the chart. All of the numbers end in 0.

- There are 10 groups of 10 in 100.

- Each number that ends in 0 was colored 3 times, once for each different method of skip-counting.

- Keeping a record on the hundred chart of their skip-counting helps to count the items by a variety of numbers, such as 3, 4, and 6.

What Might Happen . . . What to Do

Some children might make groups of 2, 5 or 10 but still count the objects by 1s. Have them first skip-count smaller quantities by 2s, 5s, and 10s and gradually increase the number until they feel comfortable skip-counting to 100.

Young children are often familiar with number names for large numbers, such as one hundred, one thousand, one million, etc. Although they can say the names, they often have no sense of the magnitude of those numbers because they have never counted or worked with that many items. This lesson develops children's sense of the quantity of 100 as well as the relative size of the number through grouping, counting, and estimating activities.

Extension

Give children a few more than 100 objects to count. Observe how they count the numbers in excess of 100. Make sure that when they get past 100, they group and count the remaining objects appropriately. For example, if they have counted to 100 by 10s, they must be careful not to continue counting single objects by 10s. Also, encourage children not to insert "and" as they say the numbers greater than 100 aloud.

Student Pages

Student page 22 has questions for the children to answer during the lesson. They use their answers to the questions in class discussion. Student page 23 contains a hundred chart for children to use as a recording sheet. It also asks children to write what they notice about coloring the chart.

Assessment

During the activities, you observed how children developed ways to organize and count 100 items. Although most children are familiar with skip-counting smaller quantities by 2s, 5s, and 10s, some children might have found the activity difficult since it involved a greater quantity. You were able to assess how using the hundred chart helped them organize their thinking. They recognized that by coloring their skip-counting on the hundred chart, they created a pattern. They used the patterns to help them predict what number would come next. This helped you determine if children were beginning to apply what they learned to higher-order thinking about numbers.

NCTM Standards Summary

Working in small groups, children used multi-sensory representations to develop a sense of the quantity of 100. They first represented 100 with physical objects and then represented the quantity symbolically on the hundred chart. Children connected their previous work with grouping, counting, and knowledge of patterns with smaller quantities to the quantity of 100. They used the hundred chart to organize and to predict what came next in counting to 100. They analyzed how grouping and counting physical objects were represented in the patterns on the hundred chart. Throughout the lesson, they communicated what they were learning to the class through discussions and through sharing their responses.

Answers

Page 22
1. Possible response: Anything close to 100.
2. Counting by 1s, 2s, 5s, 10s. Counting by 10s is the easiest and fastest way to count the large number of cubes.
3. Answers will vary.

Page 23
1. Chart should be colored to show counting by 2s, 5s, and 10s.
2. Each different way you count gives you a different colored pattern on the chart.

Learning About 100

1 Estimate how many cubes are in the bag.

_____

_____

2 What different ways can you think of to count the cubes in the bag?

_____

_____

_____

Which way do you think is best? Why?

_____

_____

_____

_____

_____

3 How close was your estimate to the number of cubes in the bag?

_____

_____

_____

Learning About 100

Use the hundred chart to count.

1 Count 100 items by 2s, 5s, and 10s. Color the squares on the chart to show how you counted. Use a different color for each way of counting.

1	2	3	4	5	6	7	8	9	10
11	12	13	14	15	16	17	18	19	20
21	22	23	24	25	26	27	28	29	30
31	32	33	34	35	36	37	38	39	40
41	42	43	44	45	46	47	48	49	50
51	52	53	54	55	56	57	58	59	60
61	62	63	64	65	66	67	68	69	70
71	72	73	74	75	76	77	78	79	80
81	82	83	84	85	86	87	88	89	90
91	92	93	94	95	96	97	98	99	100

2 What can you tell about the colored squares on the chart?

_____

_____

_____

Subtracting Two-Digit Numbers

Introduction

Objective → Children will develop a method for subtracting two-digit numbers that require regrouping.

Context → Children are familiar with trading using base-ten models. They know subtraction facts and have used the subtraction algorithm without regrouping. Children will go on to learn the standard algorithm for two-digit subtraction with regrouping.

NCTM Standards Focus

By working with concrete materials in this standards-based lesson, children experience and realize the necessity to regroup one 10 as 10 ones. Often children are shown an algorithm before they explore it concretely. In this lesson, they represent the regrouping process concretely and develop their own strategies so that when they encounter the algorithm, it will make sense to them.

Reasoning and Proof Children develop methods for subtracting two-digit numbers with regrouping and to explain how and why their methods work.

Representation Children use concrete materials or pictures to represent and model the process of subtracting two-digit numbers with regrouping.

Problem Solving Children work together to develop strategies for solving two-digit subtraction problems. They share their thinking about their methods with their classmates, listen to and question others' methods, and adjust their own.

Teaching Plan

Materials → Student pages 28–29; snap cubes

BEGIN THE LESSON BY GROUPING the children in pairs and giving them 76 snap cubes. Ask the children to make as many tens as they can. Now have one child give 48 cubes to the other child. *How many cubes do you have left?* Have children share how they separated 48 cubes from 76 and then determined how many cubes they had left. Have children record how they modeled the stages of regrouping with the snap cubes.

Methods Children Might Use

- Beginning with the groups of ten, remove 4 tens to make 40 cubes. Take out 6 ones to make 46 cubes. Then remove 2 cubes from one ten, leaving 2 complete tens and 8 ones, or 28 cubes.
- Beginning with the ones, remove 6 ones. Then separate 1 ten into ones and take 2 more cubes to make a total of 8 ones. Remove 4 tens to make 48, leaving 2 tens and 8 ones, or 28.
- Separate the cubes into 76 ones, then count out 48. This leaves 28 cubes.

Encourage children to share the methods they used to solve the problem, making sure that at least the first two methods are discussed.

The third method offers an interesting discussion. If 7 tens and 6 ones can also be thought of as 76 ones, why not as 1 ten and 66 ones, 2 tens and 56 ones, or 6 tens and 16 ones? This discussion can help to make a good connection to the formal algorithm, which will likely be presented in the very near future.

Hand out student page 28. Read the word problem aloud as the children follow along.

> Lea and her brother collect sports cards. Together they have 92 cards.
> Lea has 37 cards. How many cards does Lea's brother have?

Have children summarize the problem. *What do you need to do to find out how many cards Lea's brother has?* Direct the children to work together in the same pairs. *How could you solve this problem using the methods you used and discussed earlier?*

OBSERVE CHILDREN AS THEY WORK together and record their solution processes. Notice whether they use the methods they discussed in doing the previous problem. Encourage them to use a number sentence to show the operation they used and to record the steps they took to subtract. Suggest that they can draw pictures to explain their process and that they should be prepared to show how their answer makes sense.

When children are finished, have them share their results and methods. Encourage them to question each other about methods or steps they do not understand or that do not make sense to them. Children's solutions should show an understanding of the concept of regrouping to subtract.

Methods Children Might Use

- Represent the subtraction sentence with pictures grouped by tens and ones. Cross out 3 groups of ten and 7 ones. There are 5 groups of ten and 5 ones, or 55, left. (Children might follow this same process using snap cubes.)

- Represent 92 as 9 tens and 2 ones. Remove 3 tens from 9 tens. Then remove one more ten and separate it into 10 ones to get a total of 12 ones. Remove 7 ones from the 12. Since there are 5 tens and 5 ones left, $92 - 37 = 55$.

- Write the subtraction sentence $92 - 37 =$ _____. Count up by 10s from 37 to 87 to get 5 tens. Count up 5 ones from 87 to 92. Five tens and 5 ones is 55.

- Use the standard algorithm and show an informal regrouping notation.

If some of the children understand the standard algorithm, encourage them to explain it to the class in their own words. This can serve as an introduction to lessons on the subtraction algorithm.

What Might Happen . . . What to Do

Some children might represent the number sentence correctly but do the subtraction incorrectly. They might possibly subtract in one of the two ways shown.

$$
\begin{array}{r} 92 \\ -\ 37 \\ \hline 65 \end{array}
\qquad
\begin{array}{r} 92 \\ -\ 37 \\ \hline 62 \end{array}
$$

In the first example, they take the larger number (7) in the ones column and subtract the smaller number (2) from it. Then they subtract the tens. In the second example, they simply subtract both the 3 and the 7 from 9, because 9 is the greater number in the subtraction. Encourage children to tell what they did. Then suggest that they use groupings of tens and ones to solve the problem. Have them represent the problem using snap cubes and then draw pictures to show what they did. If necessary, provide children with extra problems and let them work together to solve them using concrete materials.

Have children work on the second problem. Observe whether their methods become more efficient.

The main objective of this lesson is to have children begin to understand the concept of regrouping using tens and ones and to apply this understanding to subtraction problems. The goal is not to have children come up with their own methods for subtracting, but to practice regrouping by tens and ones so they can apply what they learn to the standard subtraction algorithm in upcoming lessons.

Student Pages

Student page 28 contains the problems to be used for the in-class activity. Student page 29 contains two practice problems that may be assigned for individual homework practice or for additional class practice.

Assessment

As you observed the children during the class exercises and listened to their discussion of their methods, you were able to assess whether they had internalized the concept of subtraction. You were also able to assess their understanding of the concept of regrouping and how they applied this method to solve subtraction problems. Specifically, you were able to evaluate how children represented subtracting two-digit numbers with regrouping by using snap cubes and then by drawing pictures. The problems on student page 29 helped you assess an individual child's progress.

NCTM Standards Summary

Children focused on problem-solving methods as they explored ways to subtract using regrouping. They developed their understanding of the regrouping process by using snap cubes to represent subtraction problems and by drawing pictures to show what they did. Using their reasoning skills to think through their methods, they drew or wrote out the steps they used to solve the problems. They reasoned and proved that the methods they used worked by sharing them with the rest of the class and by explaining how and why their methods worked.

Answers

Page 28
1. 55 cards
2. 23 bottles of juice

Page 29
1. 29 trucks
2. 37 red beads

Subtracting Two-Digit Numbers

Show how you solved the problem. Use words and pictures.

 Lea and her brother collect sports cards. Together they have 92 cards. Lea has 37 cards. How many cards does Lea's brother have?

 There were 61 bottles of juice on a store's shelf. Shoppers bought 38 bottles during the day. How many bottles of juice were still on the shelf?

Standard 1 Number and Operation

Subtracting Two-Digit Numbers

Solve each problem. Show how you solved it.
Use words and pictures.

 Erik counted 56 cars and trucks in the parking lot. There were 27 cars. How many trucks were there?

❷ Anne is making friendship bracelets out of white and red beads. She has 80 beads in all. She has 43 white beads. How many red beads does she have?

Investigating Multiplication

Introduction

Objective → Children will develop an understanding of the concept of multiplication through the use of models and representations, which involve combining equal groups.

Context → Children have added multiple addends as well as used repeated addition. They will continue working with multiplication of small factors.

NCTM Standards Focus

Encouraging children to investigate concepts helps them develop a solid foundation on which to build future learning as well as connect to concepts they already understand and use. In this lesson, they connect the concept of addition to the concept of multiplication by representing problem situations with physical objects or their own notation. Children are often asked to comprehend new concepts worked out symbolically on the printed page. Without making connections to previous concepts, they end up memorizing the algorithms. If children never really understand how the different algorithms are developed and why they work, they may experience difficulty later as they are asked to solve increasingly complex problems.

Connections Children make connections between adding equal-sized groups, repeated addition, and multiplication.

Representation Children use objects, pictures, and numbers to represent situations in which they combine groups of equal size.

Communication Children communicate their understanding of multiplication as combining equal-sized groups. They also learn some language that can be used to indicate multiplication. Children share their methods with the class and listen to and question the methods of their classmates.

Teaching Plan

Materials → Student pages 34–35; chart paper; cubes; counters; and other countable objects

HAVE CHILDREN BRAINSTORM items that come in twos (pairs) and list their suggestions on chart paper. They might list hands, feet, ears, eyes, and so forth. Ask 5 children to stand in front of the class. *How many shoes are these children wearing?* After the 5 children have sat down, ask all the children to work out the problem. Have counters and cubes available for children to use. Remind them to show their work. As you circulate among the children, observe how each child solves the problem and the strategies he/she uses.

Methods Children Might Use

- Using counters, cubes, or pictures, they represented the shoes of the 5 children as 5 groups with 2 counters, cubes, or pictures in each group and counted the physical objects or pictures by ones.
- Skip-counted by 2.
- Represented the total number of shoes with an addition sentence;
  $2 + 2 + 2 + 2 + 2 = 10$
- Used a multiplication sentence: $5 \times 2 = 10$.
- Used a function table:

children	1	2	3	4	5
shoes	2	4	6	8	10

Note that the methods children use may be influenced in part by the time of the school year in which this lesson is presented.

CONTINUE THE LESSON BY ASKING CHILDREN to tell about things they know that come or are packaged in groups. Have children list their suggestions on separate pieces of chart paper.

Things that Come in Twos	Things that Come in Threes	Things that Come in Fours	Things that Come in Fives
socks shoes eyes arms legs ears gloves	Juice boxes Packs of pens Rolls of wrapping paper Cassette tapes	Sets of chairs Dogs' or cats' legs Playing card suits	Fingers on a hand Toes on a foot Points on a star

Pose the following problem to the class. *How many fingers are there on 4 hands?* Have children solve the problem, reminding them to show what they did to get the answer. Observe children as they work. Ask questions about what they have already done, what they are doing next, and why. Have children share the ways in which they represented the groups. *Was it necessary for you to draw fingers or was it enough to represent the fingers with lines or dots?*

f.y.i.

Tape the pieces of chart paper to the walls of the classroom and have children add to the list when they have a new idea. You can use these charts throughout this lesson as well as in later lessons.

HOLD A BRIEF DISCUSSION where the children share their solutions and strategies. Encourage them to ask questions of each other, especially if they do not understand some of the strategies their classmates used.

During the lesson, encourage children to use the language "groups of (the number)." Help them connect the word "of" to the operation of multiplication. For example, "How much is 3 groups of 4?" translates into the multiplication sentence $3 \times 4 = \square$. This will help children to understand when multiplication is being communicated to them in a problem situation.

What Might Happen . . . What to Do

Some children might rely on counting by ones to solve the problem. To help them build confidence and become more efficient problem solvers, encourage them to work together to try some of the strategies they have heard about in the class discussion. Tell them they can then use counting by ones to double check their answers.

CONNECT THE MULTIPLICATION SENTENCE to the repeated addition sentence. Write $5 + 5 + 5 + 5 = 20$ on the board or overhead. Discuss with children what each 5 represents. After they have read it out loud, point out that it takes a long time to say and write. *How else could you show this same problem?* Write "4 fives equals 20" on the board. *How could you show this in a multiplication sentence?* Have a child volunteer the answer. Then write $4 \times 5 = 20$ below the addition sentence. *How are these two number sentences alike? How are they different?* Help children make the connection between these two representations. Encourage them to see that multiplication is a faster way to show repeated addition.

Have children compare the two problems they have solved so far. *How are the shoe problem and the finger problem alike?* Encourage children to explain that in each problem they are dealing with equal groups. Have children reiterate how they can represent and solve these problems. They should conclude that equal groups can be represented using pictures or models and then solved by counting, skip counting, adding, or multiplying.

Methods Children Might Use

- Drew 4 sets of 5 fingers and counted the sets by 1s or skip-counted by 5s.
- Represented 4 sets of 5 with counters or cubes, then counted the items.
- Used a number sentence: $5 + 5 + 5 + 5 = 20$.
- Wrote "4 groups of 5" or "4 fives" and skip-counted to get the product.

Student Pages

Student page 34 contains application problems involving equal groups. Student page 35 contains additional application problems as well as a writing question about how a problem shows both addition and multiplication.

Assessment

During the lesson, you observed and questioned the children about their solution processes. You assessed how they represented equal groups in the problems using models or symbols and how they obtained their answers. Their recording and sharing gave you a picture of their understanding of when and why to use multiplication. Through your questioning, the children summarized how a repeated addition problem could be shown as a multiplication sentence.

NCTM Standards Summary

Using representation, children drew pictures, manipulated physical models, or wrote number sentences to solve problems with equal groups. Children used communication as they shared what they had found out about multiplication and repeated addition. They discussed and listened to the findings of others and adapted their own methods when it made sense. Children made connections to their prior knowledge of counting, skip counting, and multi-addend addition.

Answers

Page 34

1. $2 + 2 + 2 + 2 + 2 = 10$; or $5 \times 2 = 10$
2. $5 + 5 + 5 + 5 = 20$; or $4 \times 5 = 20$
3. $3 + 3 + 3 + 3 = 12$; or $4 \times 3 = 12$
4. $4 + 4 = 8$; or $2 \times 4 = 8$

Page 35

1. $3 + 3 + 3 + 3 + 3 = 15$; or $5 \times 3 = 15$
2. $3 + 3 + 3 = 9$; or $3 \times 3 = 9$
3. $4 + 4 + 4 + 4 + 4 = 20$; or $5 \times 4 = 20$
4. $6 + 6 + 6 = 18$; or $3 \times 6 = 18$
5. Answers will vary.

Investigating Multiplication

Solve each problem. Show your work.

 1 How many shoes are there? _____

2 How many fingers are there? _____

3 How many juice boxes are there? _____

4 How many legs are there? _____

Standard 1 Number and Operation

Investigating Multiplication

Solve each problem. Then write a number sentence for each problem.

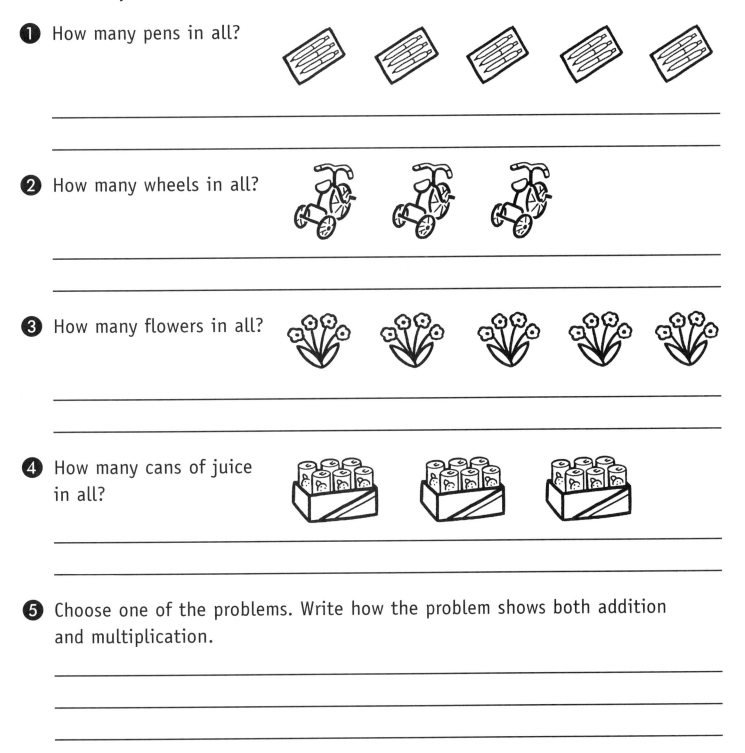

1 How many pens in all?

_____

_____

2 How many wheels in all?

_____

_____

3 How many flowers in all?

_____

_____

4 How many cans of juice in all?

_____

_____

5 Choose one of the problems. Write how the problem shows both addition and multiplication.

_____

_____

_____

Recording Two-Digit Numbers

Introduction

Objective → Children will record a number as tens and ones.

Context → In previous lessons, children have used a variety of materials to make and count groups of ten. Subsequent lessons may include recording 3-digit numbers as hundreds, tens, and ones.

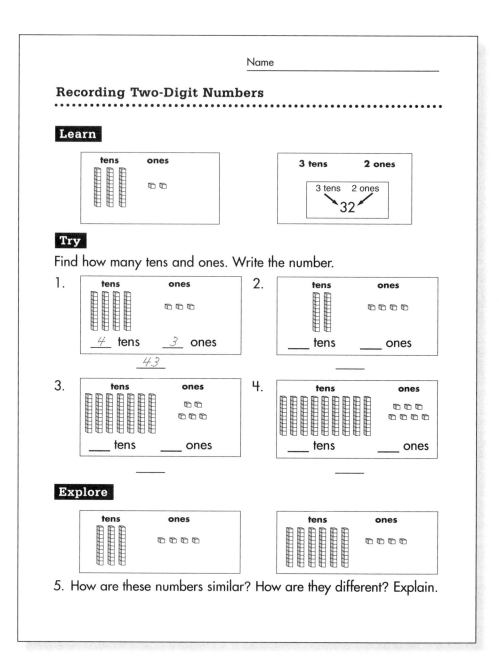

Name _____

Recording Two-Digit Numbers

Learn

tens	ones

3 tens   **2 ones**

3 tens   2 ones
32

Try

Find how many tens and ones. Write the number.

1. tens   ones
    _4_ tens   _3_ ones
    _43_

2. tens   ones
    ___ tens   ___ ones

3. tens   ones
    ___ tens   ___ ones

4. tens   ones
    ___ tens   ___ ones

Explore

tens   ones

tens   ones

5. How are these numbers similar? How are they different? Explain.

NCTM Process Standards Analysis and Focus

The standards analysis examines how the process standards have been incorporated into the above lesson. By increasing the focus on three of the process standards, a more effective and meaningful lesson can be presented. The suggestions offered can help you to think about how this might be accomplished.

Problem Solving The lesson asks children to look at pictures of cubes arranged in tens and ones and tell how many cubes there. However, the activity requires little more than filling in the blanks.

Suggestion → Have children figure out the best way to group items to count them. This type of activity allows children to experience firsthand the benefits of grouping items for identify-

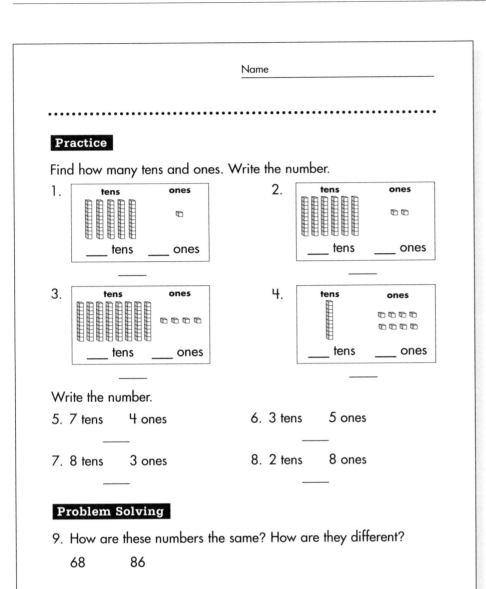

Name _____

· ·

Practice

Find how many tens and ones. Write the number.

1.
| tens | ones |
___ tens ___ ones

____

2.
| tens | ones |
___ tens ___ ones

____

3.
| tens | ones |
___ tens ___ ones

____

4.
| tens | ones |
___ tens ___ ones

____

Write the number.

5. 7 tens   4 ones

____

6. 3 tens   5 ones

____

7. 8 tens   3 ones

____

8. 2 tens   8 ones

____

Problem Solving

9. How are these numbers the same? How are they different?

68   86

ing and recording numbers. Encouraging children to actively seek solutions allows them to formulate and test their ideas.

Communication Opportunities for children to extend their understandings through discussion are limited. Questions in the teacher notes call for one-word responses and come at the end of the lesson.

Suggestion → Include small-group investigations and whole-class discussions to encourage children to articulate their ideas and strategies. Investigating various ways to group and talking about results will strengthen children's understanding of the critical role grouping by tens plays in our number system.

Representation Children are shown pictures of grouped items and

throughout the lesson are encouraged to use cubes to complete the problems.

Suggestion → Have children experiment with different groupings of connecting cubes to see which grouping makes counting easiest. This should help children better understand the relationship between grouping by tens and the method we use to record numbers.

Reasoning and Proof Children are asked to compare two-digit numbers in which the digits are reversed.

Connections An interesting connection for children is made between the number of fingers and counting by ten.

The teaching plan that follows shows how the suggestions for increasing the focus on the process standards can be implemented.

Revised Teaching Plan

Materials → Large plastic containers; connecting cubes; index cards; pencils

Teaching the Lesson

CREATE FIVE OR SIX STATIONS AROUND THE CLASSROOM. At each station, place a supply of index cards for recording numbers and a container holding more than 21 but fewer than 99 connecting cubes. Vary the number of cubes at each station.

Introduce a problem-solving activity that will lead children to understand why grouping by tens is a critical concept for understanding the base-ten system. *At each station, you'll find a container filled with connecting cubes. Work in your group to organize the cubes so that another group can easily recognize and record the number.*

Organize children into five or six small groups, assigning each group to one station. Allow time for group members to discuss and try out different ideas for grouping the cubes in their container.

Ring a bell or tap sticks to signal that it's time to stop the activity and move to the next station. When children reach the next station, give them 15–20 seconds to look at the groupings. Have each child record the number of cubes on an index card.

HAVE GROUP MEMBERS DISCUSS AND COMPARE their numbers. Encourage children to talk about how they figured out the numbers. *How were the cubes grouped? Did the grouping help you identify the number? Why? Why not?*

Add or remove cubes from the containers to change the numbers. Repeat the activity three or four times before bringing the class together to discuss the purpose of the activity: grouping by tens to identify and record numbers.

What Might Happen . . . What to Do

None of the groups organizes their cubes into groups of ten. Use cubes and an overhead transparency to model grouping by tens. Encourage children to compare this grouping system with their own. Work with children to determine which grouping worked best to help them identify the specified number of cubes.

DEMONSTRATE DIFFERENT WAYS to group 23 cubes, using a chart or overhead transparency. Group the cubes by threes, fives, and tens, each time recording the total number below the grouping. Discuss why grouping by tens makes it easier to identify the number. Draw children's attention to the tens and ones groupings. Make connections between the grouping activity and the position of each digit and how this reflects our base-ten number system.

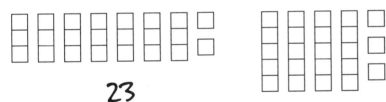

23

23

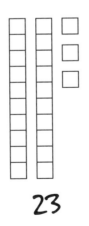

23

WRITE 43 ON THE BOARD. Provide cubes and ask children to show the number 43. In the meantime, draw 3 tens and 4 ones on the board. *Is the way you showed 43 at your desk the same way that I've drawn it on the board? Have I shown 43? What number does my grouping represent?* Children should be able to tell you that 34 is represented on the board. Record the number 34 next to your drawing. *How should I show 43? Make a drawing that shows 43. Is this what you have? How are the numerals 34 and 43 alike? How are they different?* Questions like these encourage children to think about the importance of place value. The discussion becomes a forum for children to listen to ideas and reinforce their understandings.

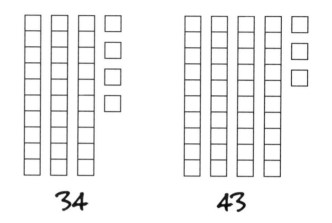

34   43

CONCLUDE THE LESSON by explaining that the base-ten system helps us to read, write, and manipulate large and small numbers and that this system stresses the importance of the placement of each digit. Reinforce children's understanding that the position of a digit represents its value. As an example, write the numbers 27 and 72. *How are these numbers alike? How are they different?*

Student Pages

Children are now ready to complete exercises similar to those on the reduced student pages.

Assessment

Both the small-group activities and whole-class discussions offered opportunities to informally assess children's thinking about how grouping helps to determine number and relates to recording numbers. Observing as children organized their cubes into groups of tens and listening to the rationale for their groupings as they shared their ideas with their classmates, provided further insights into their thinking.

NCTM Standards Summary

The lesson provided children with opportunities to investigate the underlying rationale for grouping by tens. Children were presented with a problem to solve, which gave them a context to formulate and test out their ideas. Throughout the lesson, children had many opportunities to organize connecting cubes into groups of tens. This helped children better understand the relationship between grouping by tens and recording numbers. The activities and follow-up discussions allowed occasions for children to communicate their ideas and thoughts about our base-ten system.

Standard 2 **Algebra**

A T THE SECOND GRADE LEVEL, algebra includes work with comparing numbers, understanding equality, the concept of multiplication, and using patterns. Our lessons are derived from these important topics, and include a lesson on identifying numerical relationships, a lesson on using the equal symbol, a lesson that develops the concept of multiplication, and a lesson on using patterns to solve problems.

Three lessons model how the process standards can be used to teach content. A fourth lesson is a hypothetical textbook lesson that we have revised to be more standards based. These four lessons do not represent the entire curriculum, but rather provide glimpses of how, with a more concentrated effort to incorporate the process standards, better mathematics teaching and learning can be achieved.

One lesson we have chosen has children interpret word phrases that describe relationships between numbers. The process standard of representation is emphasized in this lesson as children use manipulatives to model different word phrases and numerical relationships. Children also learn how to represent these relationships symbolically.

Another lesson we have chosen helps children develop a conceptual understanding of equality and the meaning of the equal symbol. Through the process standards of connections, representation, and communication, children use the equal symbol in familiar contexts. Children also learn about inequality, and when not to use the equal symbol.

A third lesson we have chosen has children solve problems that develop the concept of multiplication. Children can use manipulatives, pictures, words, and symbols to help them model the problem situations. By making connections to their prior experiences with addition and repeated addition, children develop new strategies to solve new problems.

The hypothetical textbook lesson we have chosen to revise is one in which children use information they find in patterns to solve problems. By presenting a problem-solving situation, children are compelled to analyze patterns. Through better representation and communication, children discuss how to approach the problem in order to arrive at a solution.

Standard 2 Lessons

Identifying Numerical
Relationships

Using the Equal Symbol

Exploring Multiplication

Using Patterns

Identifying Numerical Relationships

Introduction

Objective → Children will interpret word phrases that describe relationships between numbers and express the comparisons using numbers and operations.

Context → Children are familiar with addition and subtraction facts. They have used number sentences, dealt with doubling facts, and have explored addition and subtraction of equal groups. They have also compared quantities related to measurement and number. They will go on to extend their understanding of language and numbers as they learn about multiplication and division.

NCTM Standards Focus

In this lesson, children use concrete materials as they move from verbal descriptions of numerical relationships to expressions involving numbers and operations. By developing their own interpretations of word phrases rather than being told how to use descriptive language, the children become more aware of the mathematical significance of verbal expressions.

Representation Children use concrete materials to represent numerical relationships and then use symbolic representation. By using manipulatives, children clarify the similar quantitative meaning of different word phrases.

Communication Children analyze the mathematical ideas expressed by language. As they share their thoughts and listen to others, children become aware of a variety of ways to express comparisons.

Connections As children interpret verbal descriptions in the lesson, they also have the opportunity to reinforce graphing skills and connect verbal and visual comparisons.

Teaching Plan

Materials → Student pages 48–49; color tiles or other manipulatives that are available in red, green, blue, and yellow; small index cards or stick-on notes (optional)

HAVE CHILDREN WORK in groups of two to four and provide each group with an assortment of color tiles. Ask them to show one group of 3 tiles and another group of 6 tiles. Tell them to compare the number of tiles in the second group with the number of tiles in the first group. *How would you explain the relationship?* Allow children a few minutes to prepare their descriptions, then compile a list on chart paper. Children may say that there are three more than, double, two times, or twice as many in the second group as the first. Have children copy the list so they can expand their vocabulary and learn to express the same relationship in different ways.

Write the number sentence 6 = 3 + 3 on the chart paper. *Does this number sentence have the same meaning as each of the descriptions you just wrote?* Discuss the correspondence with each written phrase. Emphasize that although there were different word expressions, the same mathematical expression represents all of them. *What words help you identify the operation of addition?* (more than, double)

H AVE CHILDREN MAKE two new groups of tiles, one with 7 tiles and the other with 5 tiles. Ask them to describe how the second group compares to the first group. When children are ready, write their suggestions on the chart paper. They might say that the second group has two fewer tiles than the first group. Write $5 = 7 - 2$ and ask if this sentence matches their descriptions. *What words help you identify a subtraction situation?* (less, fewer)

Continue the lesson by asking each group to build a graph showing how many tiles of each color they have. Their graphs might look something like the one below. If you wish, children can use 3×5 cards or stick-on notes for the labels.

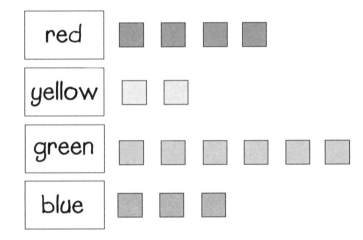

What Might Happen . . . What to Do

If children's counting skills are weak or they do not know what *more*, *less*, or *twice* means, their answers might be incorrect. Use a ten frame and have children fill in the frame with tiles in 2 colors, for example, 4 red tiles and 3 blue tiles. Discuss the number and colors of the tiles. For example, *The number of blue tiles is 1 less than the number red tiles. How many blue tiles are there?* Refill the frame and gradually introduce the lesson language.

As CHILDREN BUILD their graphs, observe them and their work. Ask how they decided to organize the graph. Then ask questions about the number relationships in the graphs.

- *How many yellow tiles are there in your graph? Which color has 2 [or 3, or 4] more tiles than yellow?*
- *How can you express the relationship between these two colors with a number sentence?*
- *Does anyone have a color that has twice as many tiles as yellow? Does anyone have a color that has half as many tiles as green?*
- *If you added 2 more red tiles, how many red tiles would you have? Write a number sentence. Would you then have more red tiles or green?*

Ask two or three groups to compare their graphs and explain how they are alike and how they are different, using the lesson vocabulary.

GIVE CHILDREN STUDENT PAGE 48 and have them each make a new color tile graph by following the directions on the page. Observe how they interpret the directions for the graph. Once the children have finished their graphs, have them answer the questions. Then bring them together to discuss what they have done. Have children tell how they created the graphs and have them explain their thinking about the questions.

Children might share some of the following observations for question 3 on page 48:

- *One fewer* means the same as subtracting one. $4 - 1 = 3$, so there are 3 blue tiles.
- *Twice as many* means the same as doubles or adding the number to itself. $3 + 3 = 6$, so there are 6 yellow tiles.
- *Two more* means to add 2. $3 + 2 = 5$, so there are 5 green tiles.

Give children student page 49 and go over the directions. Children can work on this page in class or for homework. After children have completed the page, spend some time discussing how they approached the puzzles. Encourage them to volunteer different ways they solved the problems.

Student Pages

Student page 48 contains directions for a color-tile graph and questions about the words used in the directions to describe number relationships. Student page 49 contains three number-relationship puzzles for children to solve by making graphs. They then write a puzzle of their own for a classmate to solve.

Assessment

Throughout the lesson you observed the children as they determined the number that was "one less," "twice as many," "half as many," and so on. As children interpreted the language in the problems, and used number sentences, you determined their level of understanding of the mathematical language that describes numerical relationships. You observed their ability to represent words and directions with concrete objects and then with numbers and mathematical operations.

NCTM Standards Summary

Children had many opportunities to analyze mathematical language in the directions given orally and on the student pages. They represented these directions with concrete mathematical models to solve problems. They also showed their understanding of the verbal expressions as they responded to oral and written directions. They both discussed and wrote about their understanding of the lesson vocabulary. They connected number relationships to a graphical display of information.

Answers

Page 48
1. The graph has 4 red, 3 blue, 6 yellow, and 5 green tiles.
2–3. Answers will vary.

Page 49
1. 4 red, 2 green, 6 blue, 3 yellow
2. 5 blue, 3 yellow, 9 red, 4 green, 21 all together
3. 6 yellow, 4 red, 10 green, 5 blue, 25 all together
4. Answers will vary.

Identifying Numerical Relationships

Build a color-tile graph. Use these directions.

Red has 4 tiles.   Blue has 1 fewer than red.
Yellow has twice as many as blue.   Green has 2 more than blue.

1 Draw a picture of your graph here.

2 What does your graph look like? Tell about it in writing.

_____

_____

_____

3 What words told you how to find the number of tiles to use?
Tell what the words mean. Write number sentences.

_____

_____

_____

Standard 2 Algebra

Identifying Numerical Relationships

Solve these puzzles. Make graphs with color tiles.
Each color makes 1 row of a graph. Answer the questions for each graph.

1 This graph has 15 tiles.
The red row has 4 tiles.
The green row has half as many
tiles as red.
The blue row has 3 times as many
tiles as green.
In the yellow row, there is 1 tile
fewer than in the red row.
In this graph, there are

_____ red tiles.

_____ green tiles.

_____ blue tiles.

_____ yellow tiles.

2 This graph has 5 blue tiles.
The yellow row has 2 fewer than the
blue row.
The red row has 4 more than the
blue row.
The green row has 1 more than
the yellow row.
In this graph, there are

_____ blue tiles.

_____ yellow tiles.

_____ red tiles.

_____ green tiles.

There are _____ tiles all together.

3 This graph has 6 yellow tiles.
The red row has 2 fewer than yellow.
Green has 4 more than yellow.
The blue row has 1 more than red.
In this graph, there are

_____ yellow tiles.

_____ red tiles.

_____ green tiles.

_____ blue tiles.

There are _____ tiles all together.

4 Make up your own puzzle.
Give it to a friend to solve.
Check your friend's graph.

Using the Equal Symbol

Introduction

Objective → Children will develop a conceptual understanding of equality and the meaning of the equal symbol.

Context → Children have used the equal sign as an operation signal for addition and subtraction. They will go on to use the equal sign to express equality in terms of $a + b = c$ and $c = a + b$.

f.y.i.

Children should realize that the number of ways to make 6 with addition using whole numbers is limited, but the number of ways with subtraction is limitless. If children don't make this observation, you might want to take a moment to discuss it.

NCTM Standards Focus

Many young children experience the equal sign only as a prompt to find an answer by acting on the numbers and operation signs that precede it. They need to explore and solve different expressions to understand that the equal sign does not simply mean "get the answer." In this standards-based lesson, children have the opportunity to do this. They explore the idea of equality by representing numbers and math sentences in ways that show that an equal sign does not only mean an answer is correct.

Connections Children make mathematical connections as they find different ways to represent the same quantities using the equal sign to show equality. They make connections from their earlier experiences with concrete materials to symbolic representation.

Representation Children use the equal sign to signal equivalent relationships. They strengthen their conceptual understanding of equality by exploring and representing inequality.

Communication Children communicate their understanding of equivalent relationships and the use of the equal sign. They learn and use the word *equation*.

Teaching Plan

Materials → Student pages 54–55; chart paper; cubes or other counters; scissors

WRITE THE NUMERAL 6 on a sheet of chart paper. *Can you show this number another way?* Have children brainstorm different ways to show 6 as you write the suggestions on the chart paper. Children might suggest different addition or subtraction phrases, such as $5 + 1$ or $8 - 2$. Write down 8 to 12 ways.

Continue the lesson by writing 6 in front of each suggestion. If children do not react to $6 \square 5 + 1$, for example, ask them how they could improve on it. They might want to move the 6 to make the addition sentence $5 + 1 = 6$. Rather than accommodating them, say that the 6 has to stay where it is. If children do not suggest placing an equal sign between the 6 and the addition phrase, write one in to create the addition sentence $6 = 5 + 1$.

Invite children to write equal signs in the sets of numbers on the chart paper and make true sentences. *Why do we use the equal sign in math?* Ask for different ideas until someone suggests that the equal sign tells that both sides of the math sentence show the same amount. Introduce the word *equation.* State that when an equation is true, what is written to the left of the equal sign has the same value as what is written to the right.

WHEN CHILDREN HAVE BECOME accustomed to seeing equations in the format $a = b + c$ and accept that the equal sign shows equality, ask them to look at another equation. Combine two of the addition phrases from the chart paper, joining them with an equal sign, for example, $5 + 1 = 4 + 2$. *Is this correct?* Have children answer and explain their reasons. They should conclude that both sides have a value of 6 and therefore they can be joined with an equal sign to make an equation.

f.y.i.

After you work with the number 6, you might want to have children write equations for other numbers. Tape pieces of chart paper to the walls of the classroom. Tie string to markers and attach one to each sheet. Then write a numeral as a heading on each sheet. Have children take turns writing their suggestions on the pages. You can use these pages throughout this lesson as well as in later lessons.

What Might Happen . . . What to Do

Some children might find equations such as $5 + 1 = 4 + 2$ confusing. Write the equation $6 = 6$. Get children to agree that	$5 + 1 = 6$. Replace the 6 on the left side with $5 + 1$. Get children to agree that $8 - 2 = 6$. Replace the 6 on the right side with $8 - 2$.

DISTRIBUTE STUDENT PAGE 54 and counters or cubes. Have children play the equation game on student page 54 with a partner. Explain that they will each cut out the numbers at the bottom of the page. One partner will put a number on each box on the left side of the equal sign. The other partner must choose two numbers to put in the boxes on the right side to make the equation true. The players can then use cubes to check their work. When the partners agree on an equation, they take their numbers back and write the numbers in the boxes. Partners can take turns going first.

Ask children to keep track of their methods so they can share them with the class when they have finished playing. (The methods they use will depend on when this lesson comes during the school year.)

Methods Children Might Use

- They add the numbers on the left side and choose two different numbers that make the same sum for the right side.
- They look at the numbers on the left side and make the first addend on the right side 1 less and the second addend 1 more, to keep both sums the same.
- They use cubes on the left side and then use the same amount of cubes on the right side to check that both sides are the same.
- They use the same addends on the right side as were used on the left but switch their positions (4 + 2 = 2 + 4). They explain that if the addends are the same, the sums are the same.

What Might Happen . . . What to Do

Some children might understand the concept of equality but have trouble because they make fact errors. Check to see if the children understand the concept of equality by using very small numbers such as 1 + 3 = 2 + 2. If children can explain why the expression is true but are having trouble with the lesson, chances are they do not have a firm grasp of their addition facts.

CONTINUE THE LESSON by asking children to tell about their use of the equal sign in the game. *How was it similar to what you have done before? How was it different?*

Write the following on the board:

$$4 + 3 = 5 + 1$$

Have the children discuss whether or not the statement is true. Once they have decided that it is not true, ask how they can fix it. Children might suggest changing the 4 to a 3, changing the 3 to a 2, changing the 5 to a 6, or changing the 1 to a 2.

Ask children how the statement could be corrected without changing any of the numbers. After children have had a chance to think, introduce the sign for inequality, ≠. Tell children that when you make a slash through the equal sign, the statement becomes true: 4 + 3 does not equal 5 + 1.

f.y.i.

The slash through a symbol to mean "not" should be familiar to children. They likely have seen this symbol in their everyday experiences, whether on a sign or a sticker.

CONCLUDE THE LESSON by writing several examples of equalities and inequalities on the board, but omit the equal or inequality sign. Have children draw in the signs and give reasons for their choices. Encourage them to ask each other questions, especially if they do not agree with the equations or inequalities their classmates created.

Distribute student page 55. Instruct children to use only numbers 1-9 to create equations. Consider having them write how they decided which numbers to use on the back of the page.

Student Pages

Student page 54 contains problems involving using the equal symbol to show equal groups. Student page 55 contains additional problems.

Assessment

It was possible to assess how the children represented equal groups using models or symbols as they played the equation game. Their recording and sharing provided a picture of their understanding of when to use the equal sign or the sign for inequality. As they responded to questions, the children demonstrated how they could create problems showing equality.

NCTM Standards Summary

During the lesson, children made connections to their earlier understanding of the equal sign as they learned more about equivalent relationships. They represented numbers and math sentences in different ways to show that an equal sign does not only signal that an answer is correct. To strengthen their conceptual understanding of equivalence, they investigated and identified inequalities. As they explained their equations, they communicated their representations and conceptual understandings to the class.

Answers

Page 54
1.–6. Answers will vary.

Page 55
1. 2
2. 8
3. 3
4. 4
5. 5
6. 7
7. 1
8. A combination that equals 13
9–10. Answers will vary.

Using the Equal Symbol

Create equations with a partner. Use the numbers at the bottom of the page.

Example:

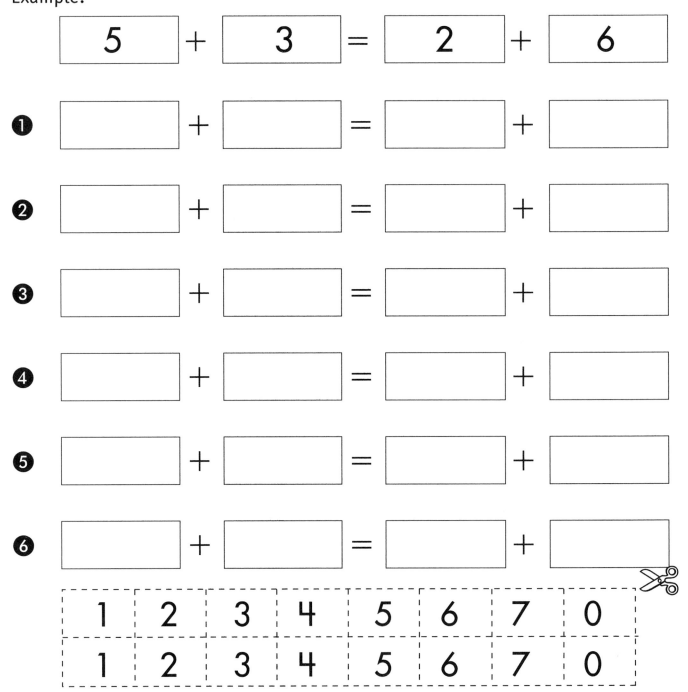

Standard 2 Algebra

Using the Equal Symbol

Complete the equations. Use numbers 1–9.

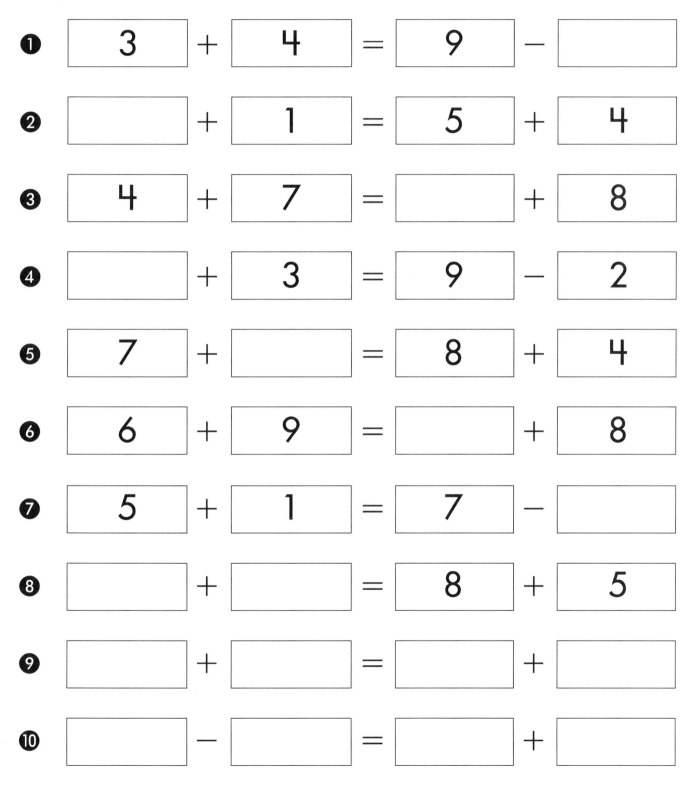

❶ [3] + [4] = [9] − [   ]

❷ [   ] + [1] = [5] + [4]

❸ [4] + [7] = [   ] + [8]

❹ [   ] + [3] = [9] − [2]

❺ [7] + [   ] = [8] + [4]

❻ [6] + [9] = [   ] + [8]

❼ [5] + [1] = [7] − [   ]

❽ [   ] + [   ] = [8] + [5]

❾ [   ] + [   ] = [   ] + [   ]

❿ [   ] − [   ] = [   ] + [   ]

Exploring Multiplication

Introduction

Objective → Children will use their sense of number to solve multiplication problems. They will use concrete materials, pictures, and words to represent the problems.

Context → Children have used addition with multiple addends. They will go on to use basic multiplication facts.

NCTM Standards Focus

Multiplication and division are usually introduced at a conceptual level at the end of second grade. However, most second graders have experienced real-world situations in which a number of same-sized groups are added together. This standards-based lesson will help children draw on and extend their understanding of combining multiple equal groups rather than focus on memorization of facts and algorithms.

Problem Solving Children build new mathematical knowledge as they solve multiplication story problems. They use problem-solving strategies to find solutions to new problem situations.

Connections Children draw on their understanding of number, part-whole relationships, and addition as they work on this lesson. They apply this prior knowledge to solve multiplication problems for which they have not yet learned procedures or algorithms.

Representation Children use concrete materials, pictures, words, and numbers to model the problem situations. They write about their methods, strategies, and solutions to show how they solved and thought about the problems.

Teaching Plan

Materials → Student pages 60–61; chart paper; cubes, counters, or other concrete materials

DISTRIBUTE STUDENT PAGE 60 and read the first problem. Encourage children to retell the problem in their own words. Have them work with a partner to solve the problem. Tell them that they can use counters or cubes, draw pictures, and write numbers and words to show what they did. Remind them of the importance of keeping a record of their thinking and the steps they take when they tackle a problem.

Give pairs of children ample time to discuss and solve the problem. Circulate among the children as they work. You might need to clarify the problem to some of the children. *What do you know about the numbers in this problem? How can this help you?* As children respond that each child in the problem has 2 feet and there's a boot or a sneaker on each foot, encourage them to represent their understanding in a way that is clear to them.

NEXT ASK THE CHILDREN to think of different ways of showing how to find the total number of boots and sneakers. After they have solved the problem, have them share their methods and solutions with the class. If other children do not ask about their methods, be sure to contribute questions. For example, if some children say they counted the footwear, ask them to describe how they counted. If they skip-counted, ask them to repeat the string of numbers aloud or to write them on the board.

Methods Children Might Use

- They might show 2 cubes for each of the 8 children and then count the cubes.

- They might draw pictures of 3 children wearing boots and 5 children wearing sneakers, and skip-count by 2s to 16.

- Using 2 for each child in the problem, they might write two repeated addition sentences: $2 + 2 + 2 = 6$ and $2 + 2 + 2 + 2 + 2 = 10$, and then add 6 and 10 to get 16 in all.

- They might add the 3 children wearing boots and the 5 children wearing sneakers: $3 + 5 = 8$ children, and then write an addition sentence with eight 2s.

- They might make a table to show the number of boots and sneakers the children wore.

Number of children	1	2	3	4	5	6	7	8
Number of shoes	2	4	6	8	10	12	14	16

HAVE CHILDREN CONSIDER the different methods that are shared. *How is this method like your method? How is it different from your method?* After children have told about and compared the methods they came up with, have them continue solving the problems on page 60. Encourage them to try one or more of the methods their classmates shared.

What Might Happen . . . What to Do

Sometimes children might not understand the question that a word problem is asking. For example, they might look at just 2 of the numbers in problem 1 on page 60, adding 3 + 5 = 8. Talk through the problem with the children and have them restate it to be sure they understand what to look for.

Children need many experiences with figuring out what information is important in a word problem and how to analyze that information. As you observe the groups solving the remaining problems, ask them to explain their methods. Follow up by asking, *What other ways can you use to solve the problem?*

Children are likely to feel comfortable with the method they chose and be hesitant to try something new. Therefore, they might not volunteer another method unless you encourage them to do so. Some children might try a few different ways, but stay with counters or cubes or pictures. Help them connect what they have done to a symbolic representation by asking, *How did you count? How can you show what you did using numbers?*

If you find that some of the children used methods that were not previously discussed, take the opportunity to pull the class together and discuss those approaches. Encourage children to ask questions about the new methods. You might ask children to use the methods on problems they have not yet solved. Be sure that they understand how the methods apply to the problems and why they work.

Some Additional Methods Children Might Use

- For problem 2, children might use a different notation: two 4s are 8 and five 2s are 10. $8 + 10 = 18$.

- They might use arrays.

```
• • • •     • •
• • • •     • •
            • •
            • •
            • •
```

- They might use the multiplication algorithm: $2 \times 4 = 8$ and $5 \times 2 = 10$.

ENCOURAGE CHILDREN TO CONNECT their use of concrete materials to pictures and symbolic notation. *How did you solve the problem? How can you show what you did using numbers?*

Student Pages

Student page 60 has word problems for children to use during the class activity. Student page 61 contains additional word problems for children to solve. You might want to send this page home as homework.

Assessment

During the lesson, you observed the children as they analyzed and solved problems involving equal-sized groups. You had an opportunity to assess their reasoning and thinking as they shared their methods and strategies with the class. Some children used concrete materials or drew pictures to represent the problem situations, while others were more comfortable using numbers and operations to solve the word problems.

NCTM Standards Summary

Working with partners, children connected and extended their prior knowledge of number, multi-addend addition, and their real-world experiences to solve multiplication problems. They applied problem-solving strategies that they learned previously to build new mathematical knowledge in multiplication. Using concrete materials, pictures and/or numbers, and operation symbols, they represented and made sense of the problem situations. They shared their representations, strategies, and solutions with the class and tried some of the methods their classmates shared as they solved additional problems.

Answers

Page 60
1. 16 boots and sneakers
2. 18 legs
3. 23 swings
4. 17 wheels

Page 61
1. 24 children
2. 26 children
3. 30 books
4. 28 shoes
5. 29 desks

Exploring Multiplication

Use counters, cubes, or numbers.
Draw pictures or write how you solved the problems.

 Today 3 children are wearing boots. 5 children are wearing sneakers. How many boots and sneakers are there all together?

 There are 2 squirrels and 5 birds around the bird feeder. How many legs are around the feeder?

 There are 3 swing sets with 5 swings each and 2 swing sets with 4 swings each. How many swings are there in all?

 There are 3 tricycles and 4 bicycles outside the building. How many wheels are there?

Exploring Multiplication

Use counters, cubes, or numbers.
Draw pictures or write how you solved the problems.

1 There are 4 tables in the art room. Each table has 3 boys and 3 girls. How many children are in the art room?

2 The class is going on a field trip. They will take 2 vans and 4 cars. The vans hold 5 children each. The cars hold 4 children each. How many children can go on the field trip?

3 The top 2 shelves on the bookcase have 8 small books each. The bottom 2 shelves have 7 big books each. How many books are in the bookcase?

4 Maria is making shoes for her stuffed toys. She has 4 dogs, 2 cats, and 2 birds. How many shoes does she need to make?

5 In the classroom, the desks are in groups. There are 2 groups of 4 desks, 3 groups of 3 desks, and 6 groups of 2 desks. How many desks are there in the classroom?

Using Patterns

Introduction

Objective → Children will use information they find in patterns to solve problems.

Context → Children have used a variety of materials to identify and create patterns. Later learning activities may encourage them to find patterns with numbers and operations.

Name _____

Using Patterns

Learn

Use a pattern to solve.
Shevonne is making a picture using 15 shapes in a row.
How many circles will she need to complete her picture?
Draw the missing shapes in Shevonne's pattern and count the number of circles.

□ □ ○ □ □ _ □ _ _ _ _ _ _ _

Shevonne needs _____.

Try

Suzanne is making a necklace out of beads. She needs 25 shapes in a row to make her necklace.
How many circle shapes will she use?
How many diamond shapes?

How are these two patterns the same?
How are they different?

Practice

1. Dorothy is painting a belt with 15 diamond shapes in a row.
   How many diamond shapes will have a dot inside?

◈ ● ◈ ◇ ◇ ● ● ● ◇ ◇ ◇ ◇ ◇ ◇ ◇

NCTM Process Standards Analysis and Focus

The standards analysis examines how the process standards have been incorporated into the above lesson. By increasing the focus on three of the process standards, a more effective and meaningful lesson can be presented. The suggestions offered can help you to think about how this might be accomplished.

Reasoning and Proof Children are asked to compare patterns and note similarities and differences.

Suggestion → Having children examine patterns to identify existing relationships will help them understand how to distinguish patterns. Asking children to make predictions about how to extend

Name _____

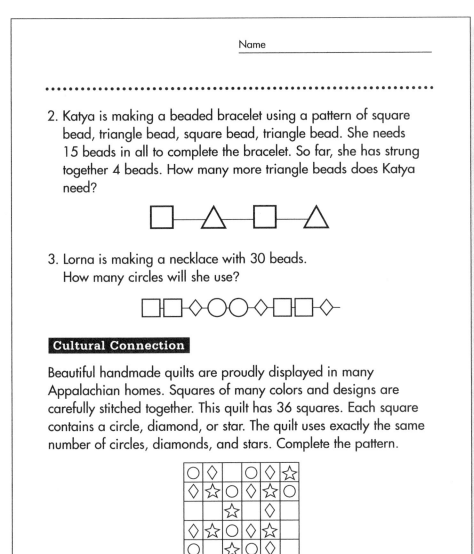

2. Katya is making a beaded bracelet using a pattern of square bead, triangle bead, square bead, triangle bead. She needs 15 beads in all to complete the bracelet. So far, she has strung together 4 beads. How many more triangle beads does Katya need?

3. Lorna is making a necklace with 30 beads. How many circles will she use?

Cultural Connection

Beautiful handmade quilts are proudly displayed in many Appalachian homes. Squares of many colors and designs are carefully stitched together. This quilt has 36 squares. Each square contains a circle, diamond, or star. The quilt uses exactly the same number of circles, diamonds, and stars. Complete the pattern.

patterns and then checking those predictions will actively involve children in their learning and reinforce their understanding.

Representation Children are asked to draw the geometric shapes used to identify pictured patterns.

Suggestion → Using concrete materials will allow flexibility while modeling and investigating relationships within pat-

terns. Having children represent patterns in a variety of ways will facilitate abstract thinking.

Communication While opportunities exist for communication that would increase understanding about patterns, they are not fully developed.

Suggestion → Encouraging children to explain their thinking as they describe pattern characteristics will help them clarify the existing relationships and

reinforce understanding. Provide opportunities for children to articulate ideas and generalize about patterns.

Problem Solving While this lesson focuses on examining patterns and answering questions about them, problem solving is not involved.

Connections A real-world connection is made as children view patterns in a design.

The teaching plan that follows shows how the suggestions for increasing the focus on the process standards can be implemented.

Revised Teaching Plan

Materials → Overhead projector; pattern blocks; counters; drawing paper

Teaching the Lesson

CREATE A SIMPLE PATTERN on an overhead projector. Select two different shapes of pattern blocks and display a segment that repeats two times. For example, show 2 triangles, 1 square, 2 triangles, 1 square. This will provide sufficient information for children to begin to understand what patterns are and to make generalizations about them.

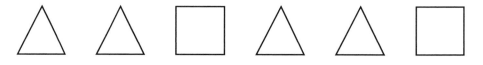

Allow time for children to observe and describe the pattern. Encourage children to share as much detailed information as possible. Descriptions might include: "I noticed 2 triangles and a square. There are three blocks in the pattern. I see 2 triangles next to each other. 2 triangles come first, then there's 1 square. There are 2 green blocks, then 1 orange block."

Work with children to brainstorm alternative ways to represent the pattern. Consider actions, letters, or shape names. For example, children might describe the pattern with claps and snaps: clap, clap, snap, clap, clap, snap. Experiencing multiple representations of the same pattern will enhance children's understanding that patterns are segments comprised of elements in an arrangement that repeats. Experiences of this type encourage children to think flexibly when they explore ideas and construct conjectures.

clap clap snap clap clap snap

A A B A A B

Distribute sets of pattern blocks to pairs of children. Have them duplicate and extend the pattern you've created on the overhead projector. *If we use this pattern and add 7 more blocks, how many more triangles will we need? How many more squares? What will the fifth block be?* Because using manipulatives allows children to make changes easily, they encourage the use of trial and error and promote investigation. Allow a few minutes for partners to discuss the questions as they work to find solutions. Walk around the room from group to group. Listen carefully as children explore and discuss possible problem-solving strategies, such as:

- Using manipulatives to represent the extended pattern, then counting how many of each
- Creating illustrations
- Using hands to reproduce the pattern: clap, clap, snap, and count. As children clap and count, they think about the shape associated with the clap or snap.
- Using fingers to count and saying the names of the shapes to keep track of the pattern
- Discussing if there are 6 blocks—that's 4 triangles and 2 squares. To make 7 blocks we need one more block. The next block would be a triangle, so that would be 5 triangles and 2 squares.

What Might Happen . . . What to Do

The last strategy begins to gener-alize an abstraction about patterns. Introduce this thinking to children if it hasn't already surfaced in the discussion. Ask children to think about the number of elements in each segment of the pattern (3). Have them consider how many elements there would be in two segments, and so on. *If we used 12 blocks, we could count by 3s and find that the pattern repeats 4 times.* Encourage children to verify this with their blocks. Draw attention to the two triangles in one segment. Demonstrate how counting by 2s four times results in a total of 8 triangles. Use blocks or counters to demonstrate and reinforce this strategy.

INVITE EACH GROUP TO SHARE its strategies and thinking processes. Highlight and discuss the different strategies children used to represent and extend the pattern. If time allows, ask a few volunteers to model or act out their solutions. Children need many opportunities to listen to and communicate their understandings about patterns. Scheduling time for informal and formal discussions helps to clarify children's understandings. Listening as classmates share strategies provides a context for children to consider alternative ways to solve problems.

Instruct children to work with their partner again. *Look at the triangle-triangle-square pattern you've been working on. Suppose there were 15 blocks altogether in the pattern; how many triangles would there be? How many squares? How do you know? How can you check your answer?* To avoid any confusion between the total number of blocks and the number being added on, be sure to emphasize that the total number of blocks children should have is 15. Have partners figure out and discuss the problem and the answer. Partner activities provide an interactive context for children to analyze and reflect on their ideas with their peers. Remind children to listen carefully to the ideas exchanged during these learning experiences. They might want to modify their first thoughts as more information emerges through the discussion.

Repeat the activity using three shapes. Have children think about different ways to represent and generate the new pattern. Multiple representations provide references for children to use as they justify and define their understandings about using patterns to solve problems.

CONCLUDE THE LESSON BY ASKING CHILDREN to create their own patterns. Encourage children to compile a list of questions about their patterns to share with classmates.

Student Pages

Children are now ready to complete exercises similar to those on the reduced student pages. The patterned design on the student pages could be used to provide another opportunity to identify one segment of a pattern.

Assessment

A number of opportunities were available to assess children's understanding of patterns. Observing and listening to children explain their thinking for extending patterns offered insights about their knowledge. Additional insights could be gleaned as children created their own patterns.

NCTM Standards Summary

Children used their ability to reason and confirm ideas as they identified relationships in patterns and determined characteristics in order to extend patterns. Children were encouraged to think about and describe patterns. They were asked to make logical predictions based on observed characteristics of patterns and then test those predictions. Multiple representations were used to model and extend patterns. Using information gained as they looked for and discussed relationships that exist in patterns broadened children's understanding of this important concept.

Standard 3 **Geometry**

AT THE SECOND GRADE LEVEL, geometry includes work with two- and three-dimensional shapes, elementary transformations, graphing on a coordinate plane, and congruence. Our lessons are derived from these important topics, and include a lesson on comparing two-dimensional shapes, a lesson introducing slides, flips, and turns, a lesson on graphing on a coordinate plane, and a lesson that focuses on congruence.

Three lessons model how the process standards can be used to teach content. A fourth lesson is a hypothetical textbook lesson that we have revised to be more standards based. These four lessons do not represent the entire curriculum, but rather provide glimpses of how, with a more concentrated effort to incorporate the process standards, better mathematics teaching and learning can be achieved.

One lesson we have chosen has children compare two-dimensional shapes. The process standard reasoning and proof drives this lesson as children describe how two-dimensional shapes are alike and different. They share their ideas both verbally and in writing. Children also work to improve their visual images of these shapes. Focusing on visual imagery helps children to think more about the differences between the shapes.

Another lesson we have chosen introduces children to the basic transformations, slides, flips, and turns. Through the process standards of representation, reasoning and proof, and connections, children will draw a given figure after applying a transformation to it, and they will also examine two shapes to see if the second is a transformation of the first.

A third lesson we have chosen is one in which children interpret information from a coordinate grid. By focusing on the process standards of representation, communication, and connections, children use words and symbols to express the location and direction of an object on a coordinate grid.

The hypothetical textbook lesson we have chosen to revise is a lesson that has children identifying congruent shapes. Through better incorporation of the process standards of problem solving, reasoning and proof, and representation, children will have more opportunities to think about and discuss congruence in different contextual situations.

Standard 3 Lessons

Comparing Two-Dimensional Shapes

Introducing Slides, Flips, and Turns

Graphing on a Coordinate Plane

Investigating Congruence

Comparing Two-Dimensional Shapes

Introduction

Objective → Children will compare and contrast the attributes of two-dimensional shapes.

Context → Children have recognized and described two-dimensional shapes in early grades. This lesson is one of the first on shapes for this grade. Children will continue with lessons on three-dimensional shapes.

NCTM Standards Focus

In this standards-based lesson, children recognize, describe, and compare two-dimensional shapes by their attributes. They use mathematical terms, reasoning, and everyday language to draw conclusions about similarities and differences between the shapes. This experience with two-dimensional shapes helps lay the foundation for work with three-dimensional shapes, as well as more formal work in geometry. It adds an interesting activity to help children work with representation.

Reasoning and Proof Children use reasoning as they describe how the two-dimensional shapes are alike and how they are different.

Communication Children use both oral and written communication as they describe and compare the two-dimensional shapes. Through this communication, they show their mathematical thinking and their mathematical understanding.

Representation Children use their visual memory to make representations of the shapes. This activity helps them focus on special characteristics of shapes. It also helps them focus on similarities and differences between the shapes.

Teaching Plan

Materials → Student pages 74–75; cut out the shapes from student page 74 for use on the overhead; overhead projector; plain white paper for children to draw

TELL CHILDREN THAT YOU HAVE TWO SHAPES on the overhead projector. Pass out sheets of white paper to each child. Tell them that you will show them the shapes for only a few seconds. They are to look at them as closely as possible; then they are to draw them.

Put a square and an equilateral triangle on the overhead. Show them for a few seconds. Give children time to draw the shapes. Ask them to talk about how they were able to remember what to draw. Ask them to tell whether one shape was easier to remember than the other. Children may mention the fact that they are familiar with the shapes. The fact that all the sides and angles were equal may have been some help to the children.

Now ask children if they know the names of these figures. List them on the board. Children may not know that the triangle is an equilateral triangle; they will probably just mention that it is a triangle. Let them know that it is a special type of triangle called *equilateral*.

Now put the names of the figures on the board. Under each figure write *differences* and *similarities*.

<table>
<tr><td colspan="2">Square</td><td colspan="2">Equilateral Triangle</td></tr>
<tr><td>Differences</td><td>Similarities</td><td>Differences</td><td>Similarities</td></tr>
</table>

Ask children to describe both the similarities and differences between the figures. Children may talk about these figures in several ways. While you want to encourage good and creative thinking, make sure that they use some of the standard terms for describing figures, such as sides and angles (or corners). This will be helpful as children compare other figures in the rest of the lesson. An important point for children to see is that the figures have a different number of sides and angles. Also, all the sides of one figure are the same length.

Children should also mention that there are different numbers of angles for each figure. The sizes of the angles are different for the square and for the triangle. But a similarity is that, for both figures, the angles are equal.

Once you are done with this example have children look at how they compared the figures. To the side of the board, start a list of what words or terms they used. It might include *sides*, *angles* or *corners*, and *space inside figures*. Tell children to think of this as you work with other figures.

What Might Happen . . . What to Do

Children may have some problem with the concept that certain things can be both similar and different. For example, the square's angles are different from the triangle's but are similar because the angles are the same in each figure.

As you work with figures like rectangles it will be important to point out that while the sides may be different lengths the two opposite sides are the same. Look for other opportunities to talk about this concept with other concepts.

---

f.y.i.

The purpose of having children draw the figures after looking at them is two-fold. First, it will work on sharpening children's visual memory. Also, it will help them start to look for the differences and similarities between figures such as side length, side relationships, and angles and their approximate measures. Children should see, as they do this activity several times, that focusing on both the similarities and differences will make it easier to remember both shapes. That is why the activity has children draw two shapes instead of one.

f.y.i.

In this lesson you will be exposing children to some terms they may not be familiar with, but, can understand, such as an equilateral triangle. It is not the purpose of this lesson for children to memorize all the names of specific figures but it is the purpose for them to see that they exist and to understand the relationship between them and other figures.

Continue this exercise with other figures. Show the figures quickly, let children draw them, and then discuss similarities and differences. As you do the lesson you may see the opportunity to make certain points by comparing certain figures. Here are some suggested figures to use to compare.

- square and rectangle
- triangle and rectangle
- square and triangle

At the end of the lesson, have children summarize what characteristics helped them remember and describe the shapes. Have them tell what each of the characteristics means. Also, have them tell about the characteristics of the different shapes they drew and compared. This discussion can lead to a definition of each shape.

Extension

If you think your class could benefit from looking at and describing three figures at once, have them try it. Make sure there are some similarities among all the figures. The parallelogram, rectangle, and square are a good set to use.

Student Pages

Student page 74 contains the shapes for use on the overhead. Student page 75 asks children to draw, describe, and compare two shapes.

Assessment

You were able to observe the children drawing, describing, and comparing shapes. In looking at what they drew, you could tell how familiar they were with some of the shapes. As they compared the shapes, you could understand both whether they recognized the shape, and how well they understood the characteristics used to describe shapes.

NCTM Standards Summary

The children used their visual memories and their knowledge about shapes and their characteristics as they tried to draw them. They used reasoning and communication as they discussed the differences and similarities among the different shapes. They characterized the shapes using mathematical terminology as well as their everyday vocabulary. Their descriptions and discussions helped them develop their mathematical thinking and understanding.

Answers

Page 74
There are no answers.

Page 75
Answers may vary.

Comparing Two-Dimensional Shapes

Shapes for Overhead

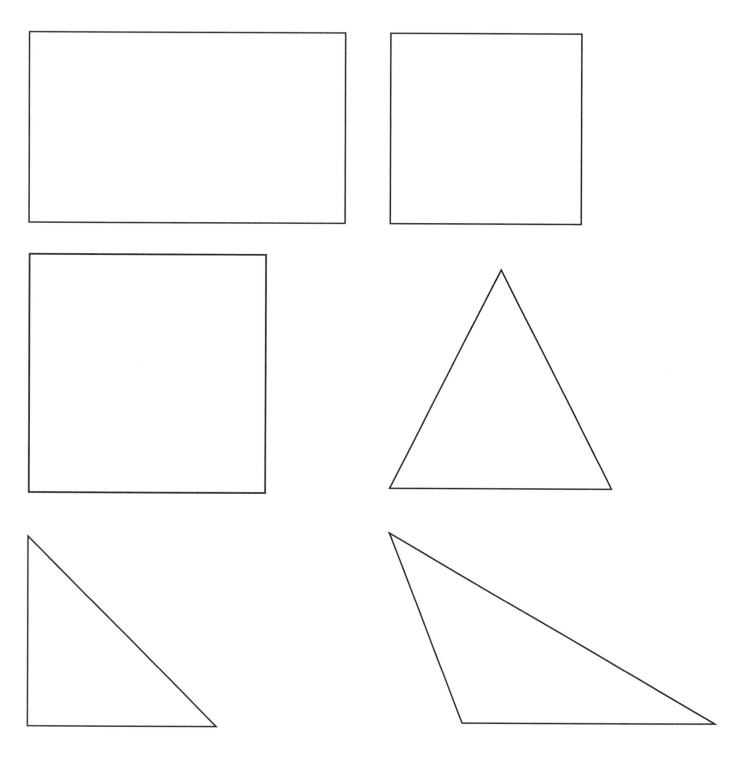

Comparing Two-Dimensional Shapes

Tell how the shapes are alike and how they are different.

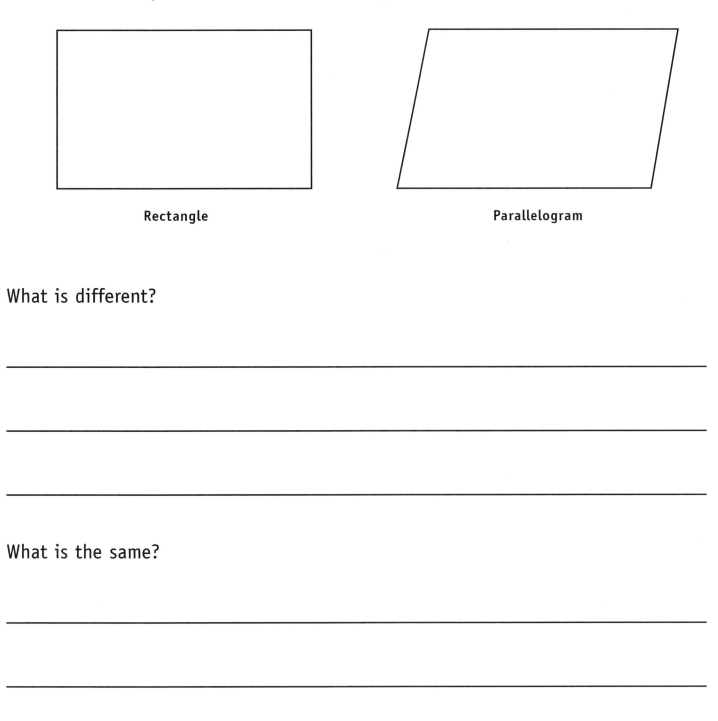

Rectangle   Parallelogram

What is different?

_____

_____

_____

What is the same?

_____

_____

_____

Introducing Slides, Flips, and Turns

Introduction

Objective → Children will learn the meaning of the terms *slide*, *flip*, and *turn*. They will interpret a figure as a slide, flip, or turn of an original figure.

Context → Children know the basic geometric shapes and can describe the similarities and differences between shapes. This is the first lesson on slides, flips, and turns. Later children will make patterns using slides, flips, and turns.

f.y.i.

You may wish to have a prescribed workspace for children so you can give them directions, such as, *Slide your triangle to the edge of your desk.* If natural work boundaries are not available, consider using a piece of construction paper as a workmat.

NCTM Standards Focus

In this standards-based lesson, children will explore different transformations of shapes. Children will learn the conventions for creating slides, flips, and turns, and they will focus on making slides, flips, and turns accurately. Then they will examine transformations and determine whether a slide, flip, or turn has occurred.

Representation Children use representations to create slides, flips, and turns. They analyze different representations of the same shape to determine what transformation has happened to the shape.

Reasoning and Proof Children analyze the transformation and use their reasoning skills to determine whether a slide, flip or turn has been made. They explain how they know they are correct.

Connections Children connect appropriate terminology with altered orientations of a figure to identify slides, flips, and turns.

Teaching Plan

Materials → Student pages 80–81; a triangle for each child (See pattern on page 80—you may wish to reproduce it on heavier paper.); an enlarged version of the student triangle for you to use for demonstration purposes

HAVE CHILDREN WORK INDIVIDUALLY at their desks or tables. Tell children that today they will be investigating three different ways to move shapes. Acknowledge that there are many ways to move shapes of figures, but point out that today the children will be focusing on three "special" ways to do this.

Give a triangle to each child. The isosceles right triangle is a good shape to use for this lesson because it has one right angle that can help children more easily identify its position. Begin by asking children what it means to slide. Ask them to talk about experiences they may have had with sliding. Then ask them what it would look like if they were to slide the triangle.

Demonstrate how to slide the triangle on the overhead or board. It is important that children understand two things about sliding the triangle:

- The triangle does not turn when it slides. After a triangle slides it will be on a different part of the workspace, but it will be facing exactly the same way it faced before the slide.

- The triangle can slide in any direction.

Show children some examples of "incorrect" slides. Have them identify why the way you moved the triangle was not an example of a slide.

Let children take some time making slides on their own. Then ask them to put their triangles in the middle of their workspace. Ask them to slide their triangles to the right about the distance of one triangle. Continue having children slide their triangles as you give different directions for them to follow. Model each slide for children. Take a moment at the end of each slide to make sure that children's triangles are in the correct position. Allow children to make corrections as needed. Remind children who are making errors that the triangle should not be turned.

NEXT, TELL CHILDREN they are going to look at another way to move the triangle. The move is called a "flip." Begin by asking children what it means to flip an object. Ask them to talk about experiences they may have had with flipping objects, such as flipping a coin or flipping a pancake. Then ask them what would happen if they were to flip the triangle.

Show children how to flip their triangles. Figures can be flipped over any line. However, with this activity it is probably best to stay with simple flips along a vertical or horizontal axis. Figure 1 shows a triangle flipped over a vertical axis. Figure 2 shows a triangle flipped over a horizontal axis.

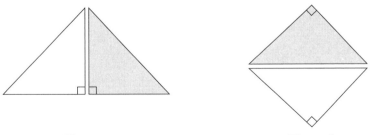

Figure 1   **Figure 2**

As you did with slides, give children directions and ask them to flip their triangles as you model the flip for them. At the end of each flip, give children time to compare the position of their triangles to yours. Allow children to make corrections as needed.

NOW TELL CHILDREN they are going to look at a third way to move the triangle. The move is called a "turn." Ask children what it means to turn and what they have seen that makes turns. One of the important things to stress with children about turns is that when they turn a figure there is a turning point. To show this, ask each child to stand up and make a right turn on his or her right heel. Help children see that although they have turned, their heels did not leave the ground. Even though they are facing in a different direction their heels are in the same spot.

Figures can be turned about any point. However, for this activity, it is probably best to stay with simple turns about a vertex. The figure below shows three rotations of a triangle that have been made around a vertex.

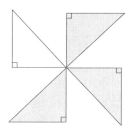

Using your triangle, model some turns for the class and have children make turns along with you. In each case, tell children what point you are using as a turning point. As with slides and flips, take time to make sure children's triangles have the correct orientation.

CONTINUE THE LESSON by having children play a game called "What Happened to Me?" Explain that you will trace around a shape using the overhead or the chalkboard to show the starting position. Then, you will ask them to close their eyes while you create a slide, a flip, or a turn, and trace around the new position of the shape. You will ask them to open their eyes and look at the two traced figures and tell you what was done to the shape. As children respond, have them explain how they know which transformation occurred. Play this game with the children until you are confident that they can identify simple slides, flips, and turns.

CONCLUDE THE LESSON with a review of slides, flips, and turns. Assign student page 81 for class work or homework. Page 81 has problems similar to the ones children did during the lesson.

Student Pages

Student page 80 contains the triangles needed for the class activities. Student page 81 ask children to examine pairs of figures and decide whether a slide, flip, or turn has occurred.

Assessment

During the lesson, you were able to observe children sliding, flipping, and turning their triangles. As children played "What Happened to Me?," you could assess whether they were able to distinguish among slides, flips, and turns. Student pages offered further evidence of children's understanding of these concepts.

NCTM Standards Summary

Children explored simple transformations of shapes on a plane. They represented the transformations physically using cutout shapes. They worked with the transformations pictorially as examined drawings and determined whether a slide, flip, or turn had been performed. They communicated their understanding of what happens to the shapes when slides, flips, and turns occur. They used reasoning as they distinguished among slides, flips, and turns, and they explained how they determined their answer.

Answers

Page 80
This page contains triangles for use during the lesson.

Page 81
1. Slide
2. Flip
3. Turn
4. Flip
5. Turn
6. Slide

Introducing Slides, Flips, and Turns

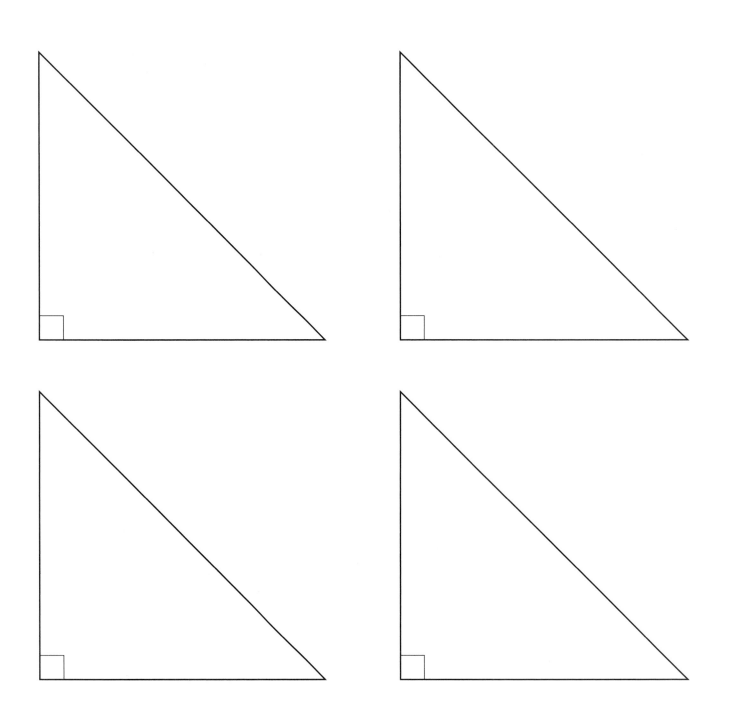

Standard 3 Geometry

Introducing Slides, Flips, and Turns

Tell whether there has been a slide, a flip, or a turn.
Use your triangle to help you.

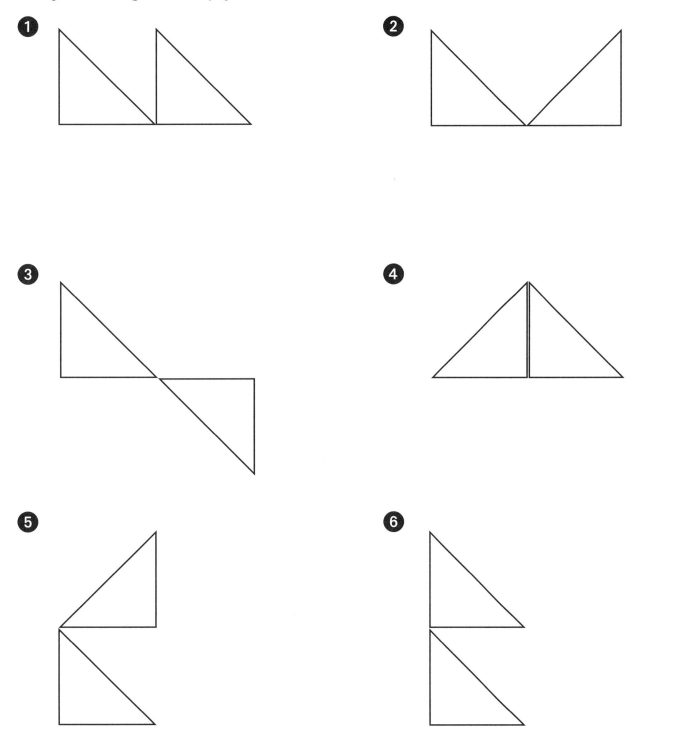

Graphing on a Coordinate Plane

Introduction

Objective → Children will interpret information from a coordinate grid.

Context → Children have used directional language as they have described movement in space. After this lesson, children will continue to work with coordinate grids.

f.y.i.

If you don't have a coordinate floor grid, you might want to use a large plastic tablecloth, a plastic shower curtain, or even masking tape to mark off a grid on the floor.

NCTM Standards Focus

In this standards-based lesson, children are at the beginning stages of representing objects in space. They will learn that in order to represent the location of an object, they must have common words and ways of communicating the placement of the object. If all people had different ways to describe the location of an object on a grid, they would not necessarily be able to retrieve the object or find its location. In this lesson there is an emphasis on the importance of communication and using correct verbal descriptions of the locations of different objects.

Representation Children use words, oral explanations, and symbols to represent the location of objects.

Communication Children describe the location of an object and directions for getting to the object. They do so by using coordinates.

Connections Children connect coordinates to a certain position on a grid.

Teaching Plan

Materials → Student pages 86–87; large coordinate floor grid; large attribute blocks; pattern blocks

Preparation → To prepare for the lesson place the large plastic floor grid on the floor. Label the grid "Shape Land." Label the horizontal and vertical axes with numbers 0 through 5. Place large attribute blocks or cutout shapes at various points on the grid. Use index cards to label the numbers on both axes. If you wish you can do this activity on the overhead.

To begin the lesson, ask children how they would describe the location of objects in the room. For example, how would they describe the location of the long rectangular table? Children's responses might be that the table is in the back of the room or next to the sink.

Choose different objects in the classroom. Have children describe the location of the objects. Encourage them to use words such as *next to*, *over*, *under*, *left*, and *right*.

INTRODUCE THE "SHAPE LAND" ACTIVITY by telling children that they are going to talk about directions and describe the locations of shapes in "Shape Land." Ask children to look at the grid. Point out the numbers on the grid and have children tell what the numbers mean. It is important that children realize that the numbers refer to the lines *not* the squares on the grid. Point out that there are lines going across and lines going up and down and that the points where lines cross are called *intersections*.

Tell the children that they are going to learn how to describe the location of different shapes that are placed on the grid.

Place a circle at the intersection of 1 across and 2 up. Inform children that the rules for walking the grid are to begin at (0, 0) and to walk along the horizontal axis (or across) and then the vertical axis (or up). A step is the length of the side of a square.

Ask a volunteer to walk 1 step across the grid and then 2 steps up to get to the circle. Make sure he or she walks slowly. Have another child describe what the volunteer is doing. Have the volunteer stop at the circle. Review with the class what the child did to get to the circle.

Now ask the children what they could call the intersection where the circle is. Discuss the different ideas the children have. Then tell them that in "Shape Land" this intersection is called (1, 2). Ask children to explain why naming the intersection (1, 2) makes sense. They should realize that (1, 2) is the intersection of the 1 at the bottom of the grid and the 2 at the side. On the board or on chart paper, record the location of the circle at (1, 2).

CONTINUE PLACING SHAPES on the grid and repeating this activity. Remind children that they need to walk on the grid to find the objects. Remind them to walk along the horizontal axis first, then turn and walk up the vertical axis. Invite the class to identify the point where each shape is located. Make sure that you place some shapes on the 0 lines, for example, (0, 2) or (1, 0). Children need to understand that (0, 0) is also part of the grid. As the activity continues, record the locations of the shapes.

After children have done the activity several times, review with them how the grid and the numbers on the grid helped them locate the shapes. Now clear all the shapes from the grid and do the activity in reverse. Give a child a shape and ask him or her to place the shape in a certain location, for example at (0, 4). Make sure you have the child tell why he or she is putting the shape at the location. This will also give you a chance to reinforce the fact that the first number tells you to go across and the second number tells you to go up.

Since many children have difficulty determining which direction to go first when looking at a pair of coordinates, you may wish to try this activity. Place a child on (3, 2) and another child on (2, 3). Have the children name each intersection and tell why the intersection has that name. Then discuss the difference between the two locations. Ask children why someone might get the intersections mixed up. Have them talk about what they can do to keep from getting mixed up.

Give children a copy of student page 86. Have them complete the page. Review the page with them. Discuss any misunderstandings or incorrectly given coordinates.

Next, give children a copy of student page 87. Have them complete the page and discuss what they did.

Student Pages

Student page 86 is a grid of "Shape Land," with a triangle, a circle, and a square placed on the grid. Children write the coordinates of the locations of the shapes. Student page 87 is an empty grid on which children place shapes according to directions given on the page.

Assessment

You observed the children as they worked on the large class grid, and located and then placed shapes. You assessed their language usage and the ease with which they determined the intersections of lines. Finally, you had an opportunity to see how they worked individually on their own grids.

NCTM Standards Summary

Children communicated their understanding of how objects were represented on coordinate grids. They communicated their understanding of the notation. They physically followed directions and communicated how the shapes were located on the grid. They used common vocabulary to explain their understanding of location and how to describe a particular location. They used communication and reasoning again as they placed shapes on given locations.

Answers

Page 86
1. (1, 1)
2. (3, 2)
3. (2, 3)

Page 87
1–4. Check children's work.

Graphing on a Coordinate Plane

Answer the questions.

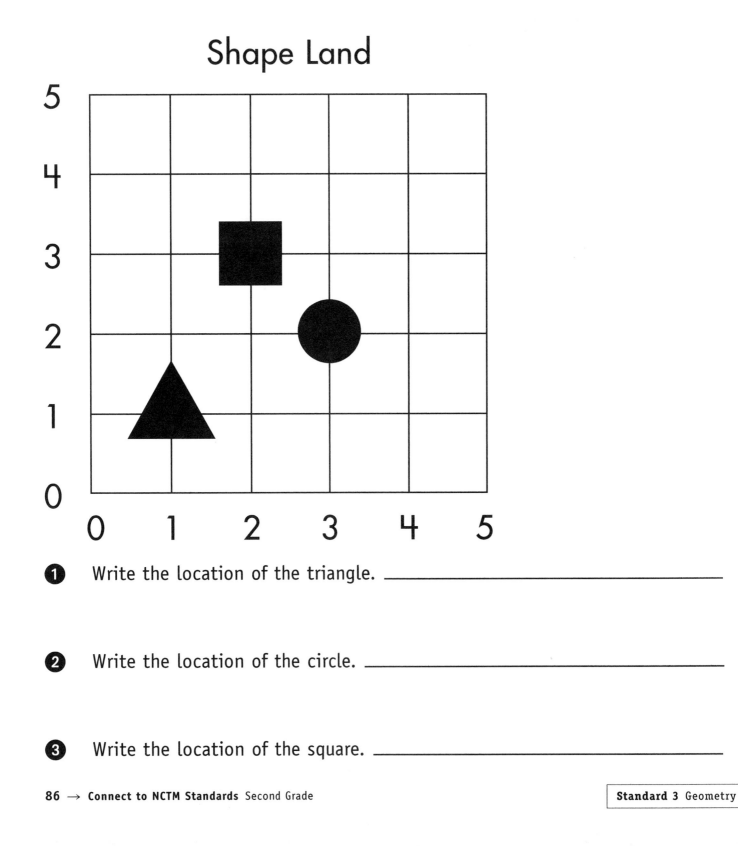

Shape Land

1. Write the location of the triangle. _____

2. Write the location of the circle. _____

3. Write the location of the square. _____

Standard 3 Geometry

Graphing on a Coordinate Plane

Put the letters in the correct place on the grid.

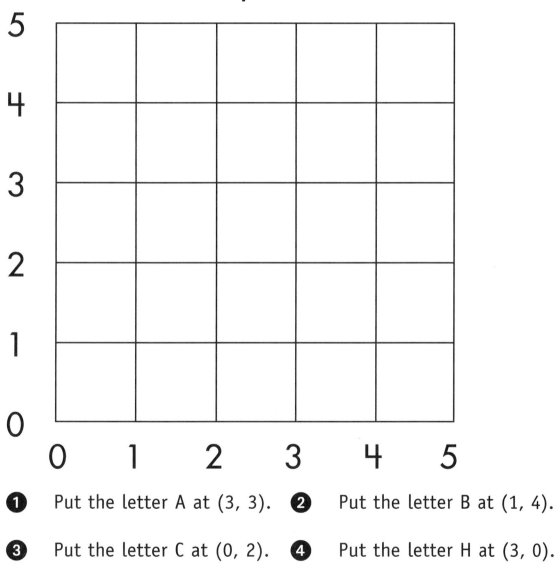

Shape Land

1 Put the letter A at (3, 3). **2** Put the letter B at (1, 4).

3 Put the letter C at (0, 2). **4** Put the letter H at (3, 0).

Investigating Congruence

Introduction

Objective → Children will identify figures that have the same size and shape.

Context → Children have identified the number of sides and angles in polygons. Future lessons include investigating lines of symmetry.

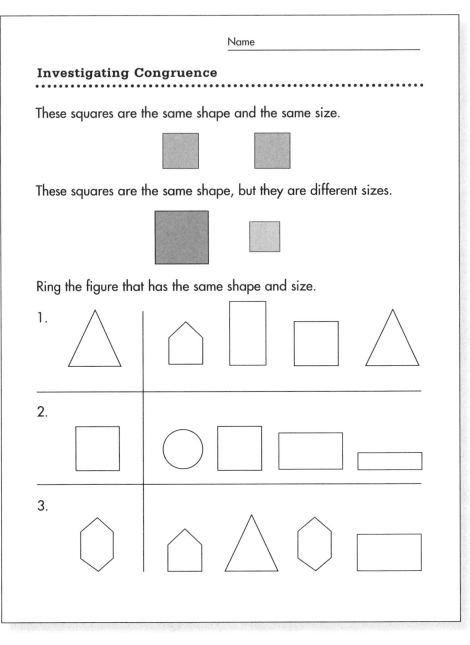

Name _____

Investigating Congruence

These squares are the same shape and the same size.

These squares are the same shape, but they are different sizes.

Ring the figure that has the same shape and size.

1.

2.

3.

NCTM Process Standards Analysis and Focus

The standards analysis examines how the process standards have been incorporated into the above lesson. By increasing the focus on three of the process standards, a more effective and meaningful lesson can be presented. The suggestions offered can help you to think about how this might be accomplished.

Problem Solving Activities involve recognizing and identifying shapes that match in both size and shape. Problem solving is not emphasized.

Suggestion → Pose problems for children to solve as they investigate congruent and similar figures. Problem-solving opportunities increase children's engagement in the activity which, in turn, will strengthen their understanding of the mathematical concepts.

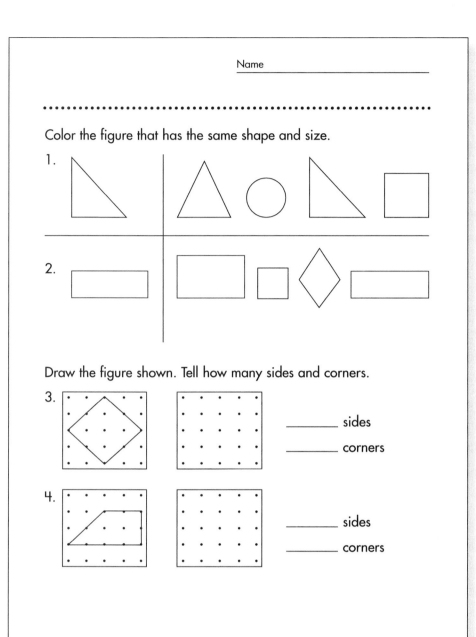

Name _____

Color the figure that has the same shape and size.

1.

2.

Draw the figure shown. Tell how many sides and corners.

3.

_____ sides

_____ corners

4.

_____ sides

_____ corners

Suggestion → **Employ a variety of manipulatives that promote active learning experiences to help children identify congruence and similarity. Projecting images on the chalkboard offers another method to examine the concepts.**

Reasoning and Proof Children are not asked to explain their thinking.

Suggestion → **Provide multiple opportunities for children to use manipulatives to create congruent shapes, and encourage children to explain how they know the shapes are congruent. Making comparisons and testing for congruence are facilitated by the use of concrete materials.**

Representation Geometric drawings are used to represent matching shapes on the student pages; however, the orientation of figures to be matched does not vary from the model. Teacher notes suggest having children sort attribute blocks, pairing those with the same size and shape to show congruence, and those with the same shape but different size to show similarity.

Communication Opportunities for meaningful discussion are minimal.

Connections Teacher notes suggest talking about shapes used in buildings but do not mention connecting that information to similarity or congruence. Utilizing children's prior knowledge or making connections to everyday situations are not included in the lesson.

The teaching plan that follows shows how the suggestions for increasing the focus on the process standards can be implemented.

Revised Teaching Plan

Materials → Per child pair: pattern blocks and a set of tangrams or attribute blocks; overhead projector; overhead transparencies of pairs of congruent shapes that are not regular, such as right triangles, house-shaped pentagons, and/or letters of the alphabet

f.y.i.

Allow sufficient time for children to look for solutions on their own before guiding them.

BEGIN THE LESSON WITH PATTERN BLOCK ACTIVITIES. Take time to review the different shapes. Hold up a block and ask children to find a matching block. Invite volunteers to name the shape and identify the number of sides and angles, or corners. Repeat with each different-shaped block. Paying attention to angles and sides helps to build awareness of the attributes to look for when considering similarity and congruency. Working in pairs should encourage children to share strategies as they solve problems.

How can we show that two of the green triangles are exactly the same size and shape? Guide children in placing one on top of the other. Children should see that the sides and corners fit exactly; the sides are all the same length and the corners are the same size. *How can we show that two blue rhombuses are exactly the same size and shape? Is it possible to use green triangles to make a figure that is exactly the same size and shape as a blue rhombus?* Guide children in putting together two triangles to make one rhombus. *How do you know that the rhombus made with two triangles is the same size and shape as the blue rhombus?* Placing the blue rhombus on top of the figure made from the two triangles will demonstrate that the sides are the same length and the angles, or corners, match. Help children to articulate these relationships. This activity reinforces the idea that congruent shapes can be created by putting parts together.

CHALLENGE CHILDREN'S THINKING and strengthen their understanding of congruence. *Can you make a figure with green triangles that is exactly the same size and shape as the red trapezoid? Can anyone suggest another way?* Help children see how combining three green triangles or one blue rhombus and one green triangle can make the trapezoid. Be sure to ask children to explain how they know that the figures are the same size and shape.

CONDUCT A SIMILAR ACTIVITY with tangram pieces. Challenge children to build the parallelogram and the medium triangle with two small triangles, and to build the large triangle using combinations of tangram pieces. Investigations of this type help develop spatial reasoning and focus attention on the attributes that need to be considered when determining congruency.

Introduce the term *congruent*, explaining that when two shapes are exactly the same size and shape they are congruent. Ask children to suggest shapes other than pattern blocks that might be congruent. Record children's suggestions. *How could we find out if the things suggested are actually congruent?*

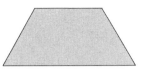

1 red trapezoid

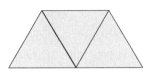

3 green triangles

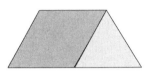

1 blue rhombus
+ 1 green triangle

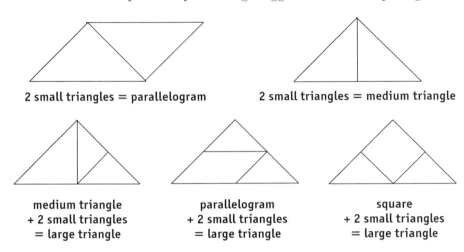

2 small triangles = parallelogram   2 small triangles = medium triangle

medium triangle
+ 2 small triangles
= large triangle

parallelogram
+ 2 small triangles
= large triangle

square
+ 2 small triangles
= large triangle

NEXT, PRESENT A PAIR OF CONGRUENT POLYGONS that are not regular on the overhead projector. Be sure to vary the orientation of the two figures. *Are these the same size and shape? How can we check?* If no one suggests rotating the figures and placing one on top of the other to see if all parts match up, demonstrate this. It is important for children to understand that the orientation of the figures is not a consideration when identifying congruence. Repeat this activity with several pairs of figures.

HAVE CHILDREN PLACE a green pattern block triangle next to a small tangram triangle. *Are these two figures the same size?* (No.) *What is the same about these figures?* (They are both triangles.) *What is different?* (The shapes of the two triangles are not the same.) Use the overhead projector to draw children's attention to the angles and sides of

f.y.i.

A regular polygon is a polygon in which all sides are equal and all angles are equal.

the figures. Rotate the shapes to demonstrate that they are not congruent. Children need to experience multiple representations of the concept to develop understanding.

What Might Happen . . . What to Do

Children might have difficulty making the distinction between a figure being triangular in shape and the different shapes a triangle might have. Remind children that the term *triangle* describes a figure that has three sides and three angles, or corners. However, there can be considerable variation in the lengths of the sides as well as the size of the angles. Draw several triangles of varying shape on the board and point out differences in their angles and sides to reinforce that all triangles do not have the same shape.

ASK CHILDREN TO PAIR TANGRAM PIECES that appear to be the same shape. Allow time for children to share their observations as they compare small triangles, small triangle and medium triangle, small triangle and large triangle, and medium triangle and large triangle. *Are all of the pairs of triangles you just named congruent?* (No.) *Why?* (Only the two small triangles are congruent. The other pairs of triangles are the same shape, but in order to be congruent, they must also be the same size.)

f.y.i.

Angle measurement is the key to similarity. Similar figures have congruent angles. The sides of the figures may be increased or decreased, but that change must occur proportionally so as not to affect the size of the angles.

Introduce the term *similar,* explaining that when objects are different sizes but are exactly the same shape, they are similar. Use the overhead projector to demonstrate this concept. Show three or four different-size squares. *Are all squares the same shape?* (Yes.) *What's the same about them?* (The corners are the same. Within each square, the sides are all the same length.) *How are these squares different?* (The sides on the different squares have different lengths.) Explain that because each angle of a square must measure 90° the angles of all squares are the same. The only thing that would change from one square to another would be the lengths of the four equal sides. While children should not be expected to internalize technical information, a simple introduction to this concept can be made.

NEXT, PLACE A SHAPE on the overhead projector so that its image is on the chalkboard. Ask a volunteer to trace the projected image. Then move the projector away from the board to enlarge the projected image. Invite another volunteer to trace the new projected image. *Are these two figures the same size?* (No.) *Are their shapes exactly the same?* (Yes.) *How do you know?* (The same figure was used on the overhead to create the drawings on the board.) Next, move the projector closer to the board and ask a volunteer to trace the smaller image. Repeat the questions. Guide children to see that the figures are indeed similar but they are not congruent.

CONCLUDE THE LESSON by summarizing the difference between congruence and similarity. Invite volunteers to use manipulatives or the overhead projector to share specific examples that illustrate their understanding of the two concepts.

Student Pages

Children should now be ready to complete exercises similar to those found on the reduced student pages.

Assessment

Learning activities with pattern blocks and tangrams provided a context to assess children's understandings of the concepts of congruence and similarity. As they created shapes and discussed the figures projected onto the chalkboard it was possible to observe children's methods and hear their thinking.

NCTM Standards Summary

Thought-provoking questions were integrated throughout the lesson to develop the mathematical concept of congruence. Small- and whole-group learning experiences aimed to develop and reinforce children's insights about the mathematical concepts. Discussions helped children to formulate concrete reasons to distinguish figures that are and are not similar. The use of manipulatives offered concrete models to visualize how figures can be the same size and shape. These hands-on activities allowed children to test out their ideas, strategies, and methods. Children saw the mathematical concepts represented in different forms. These experiences helped to clarify children's understandings and encouraged them to use representations in flexible ways when faced with problem-solving situations.

Standard 4 **Measurement**

AT THE SECOND GRADE LEVEL, measurement includes a lot of work with estimating and measuring length in both customary and metric units, estimating and measuring weight, and the concept of time. Our lessons are derived from these important topics, and include a lesson on estimating and measuring length in centimeters, a lesson on estimating and measuring length in inches and feet, and a lesson on telling time to the hour.

Three lessons model how the process standards can be used to teach content. A fourth lesson is a hypothetical textbook lesson that we have revised to be more standards based. These four lessons do not represent the entire curriculum, but rather provide glimpses of how, with a more concentrated effort to incorporate the process standards, better mathematics teaching and learning can be achieved.

One lesson we have chosen has children estimate and measure lengths of objects using centimeters. Through the process standards of representation, connections, and reasoning and proof, children use visual representations of one, ten, and twenty centimeters as benchmarks with which to estimate the lengths of other objects. They also use them to determine the length of longer objects.

The second lesson we have chosen is one in which children estimate and measure length, but using one foot as a benchmark. Through representation and connections, children develop a better sense for just how long one foot is, and how the lengths of other objects compare to one foot. Children build their estimation skills, and measure to verify their estimates.

A third lesson we have chosen is one that explores the metric weights of grams and kilograms. Children are often told what objects weigh, and are supposed to estimate about other objects based on the weights of the given objects. In this lesson, representation and connections are emphasized as children hold a one-gram weight and a one-kilogram weight to develop a better sense of how much weight each represents, then hold other objects to see how they compare in weight.

The hypothetical textbook lesson we have chosen to revise is a lesson that has children telling time to the hour, and relating time to their daily experiences. In comparable lessons, children are to write the correct time from an analog display and a digital display. With better incorporation of the process standards connections, representation, and reasoning and proof, children better relate the concept of hour to the overall scheme of time. By considering only the hour hand (eliminating the minute hand), children gain a much better sense of telling time.

Standard 4 Lessons

Estimating Length

Estimating and Measuring Length in Inches and Feet

Exploring Metric Weights

Telling Time to the Hour

Estimating Length

Introduction

Objective → Children will estimate and measure length using centimeters.

Context → Children have had experiences measuring length using nonstandard units of measure. They will continue to measure length using metric and customary standard units.

NCTM Standards Focus

Often, children simply learn rules for using standard measurement tools such as rulers, without relating the rules to the basic concept of measurement. In this standards-based lesson, children use a standard unit of measure, the centimeter, in much the same way they used nonstandard units. They work on their measurement methods just as they did with nonstandard units. In addition, they begin to internalize their understanding of the centimeter by using benchmarks and by estimating before they measure.

Representation Children view base ten cubes and long blocks to understand what 1, 10, and 20 centimeters look like. They then use centimeter rulers to find and record the exact lengths of a variety of objects.

Connections Children make connections between measuring length in lnonstandard units and in centimeters. They apply measuring methods they learned earlier to measure objects that are longer than their centimeter rulers.

Reasoning and Proof Children determine how objects of known length can be used as benchmarks to help them find other objects of about the same length. They also determine how to measure objects longer than their measurement tool.

Teaching Plan

Materials → Student pages 100–101; base ten cubes; base ten long blocks; centimeter rulers; transparent centimeter ruler; chart paper

ASK CHILDREN TO SHARE their prior experiences with measuring. *What were you trying to find out? What tools did you use to measure?* Elicit from children that most often they measured to find length, and they used nonstandard units such as straws or links. Show children a base ten cube, and place it on the overhead. Place a transparent centimeter ruler alongside the cube, and point out that the cube is as long as 1 centimeter on the ruler. Help children to restate the idea by saying that the edge of the cube is 1 centimeter long.

You may want to have a brief discussion of the difference between nonstandard and standard units. Explain that if you measure a length in centimeters, you can tell someone in another class—or another city, or halfway around the world—how long the thing is, and the person will understand. Centimeter rulers are used all over the world, so when you talk about 1 centimeter, anyone with a ruler can see that same length. If you talk about 1 straw, the other person has to look at the same straw to understand.

Now hold up a long base ten block next to the cube. *How long do you think this block is?* Place the new block below the cube on the overhead so that children can see the relationship between the two figures. Now place the centimeter ruler alongside the long block to show that the block is 10 centimeters long. Be sure to align the zero end of the ruler with the end of the block to model how children should measure.

How long do you think a shape twice as long as this ten-centimeter shape would be? While children respond, place two long blocks end-to-end on the overhead. Align the ruler with this new figure to show that it is exactly twice the length of the single long block, or 20 centimeters.

Pass out the rulers, and ask children to look at the centimeter side. Using the transparent ruler on the overhead, point out the lines and numbers representing the 1-centimeter units. Emphasize the point that measurements should begin at 0.

TAKE THE BLOCK AND CUBE from the overhead and place them where children can see them. Explain that these two objects can be points of reference, or benchmarks, for finding objects around the room that are roughly the same length as these shapes. You might note that the overhead magnifies things, so it's a good idea to look directly at the cube and block to get an idea of the lengths of 1 centimeter and 10 centimeters.

Group children in pairs. Provide them with student page 100 to use as a recording sheet. Tell them that their task is to find as many different objects as they can that measure 1 to 3 centimeters, 10 to 15 centimeters, and 20 to 25 centimeters. When they find an object that fits one of the categories, they should list it in the appropriate section. Remind them to refer to the 1-centimeter cube and the 10-centimeter block. These benchmarks will help them narrow their search. While children look for objects to measure, observe the different approaches and strategies they use.

Once children have recorded at least two objects for each length range, have them return to their seats. Record the objects they've found on a class chart,

f.y.i.

By providing a range of lengths for the objects, you increase the likelihood of success for the children. In addition, children will begin to approximate length before measuring, preparing them for the second part of this lesson.

making one column for each length range. *What did you use as a benchmark for finding objects that measured between 10 and 15 centimeters? Look at the list of objects that measured between 10 and 15 centimeters. How are they alike? How are they different?*

SELECT FOUR OF THE OBJECTS that were recorded in the 10- to 15-centimeter column. First show one of the objects to the children, then place it on the overhead. Demonstrate how to line up the object with the straight edge of the ruler (starting at 0) in order to accurately measure the length of the object. Continue with the other three objects, as needed. While doing this, you may want to ask the following questions:

- *What would happen if I started measuring at the 1 instead of the 0 on the ruler?*
- *How would I measure an object that is longer than my ruler?*
- *When you used straws or learning links for measuring, how did you find the length when the straw was shorter than the object you were measuring?*

Encourage children to make connections to their prior experiences with nonstandard units in order to work out their methods for measuring with the centimeter ruler.

Inform children that they are going to go on a centimeter hunt with their partners. Their task is to find 6 classroom items that are listed on student page 101. For each object, they should first estimate the length in centimeters, then find the actual length. They can measure any item that fits the description—for example, an eraser can be a pencil eraser, a separate rubber eraser, or a chalkboard eraser. Go over student page 101 with children and make sure they understand how to record their information. Be sure they know that *cm* is the abbreviation for *centimeter*.

Once children have completed this task, ask them to share their results. Ask about any questions they had and any problems they encountered. Have them share the strategies they used for first estimating, then measuring, their desk—the longest object on the hunt. Bring closure to the lesson by reviewing three important tips for measuring with a ruler:

- Always line up the end of your object at 0 on the ruler.
- Be sure to place the straight edge of the ruler against the object you are measuring to get the most accurate measurement possible.

f.y.i.

It is likely that the length of some or all of the objects listed on the chart will fall between centimeter units. Show children how to measure the objects to the nearest whole centimeter. If children are not familiar with this idea, demonstrate the process a few times, asking volunteers to help.

- If the object is longer than the ruler, mark the place where the end of the ruler touches the object, move the ruler so that 0 is at that place, and measure again. Add each section you measure to find the total length of the object.

Student Pages

Student page 100 provides a place for children to record the lengths of objects that measure 1–3, 10–15, and 20–25 centimeters in length. Student page 101 asks children to estimate, then measure, the length in centimeters of 6 designated items in the classroom.

Assessment

While children looked around the classroom for items in the three different length ranges, you were able to observe their use of benchmarks—whether they reasoned how to use the base ten cubes and blocks to find objects of given lengths. When the children estimated and measured the length of other items in the classroom, you noted whether they made proper use of the ruler. You were able to observe how children transferred their experiences with nonstandard units to accurately measure an object that is longer than their measuring tool.

NCTM Standards Summary

Many measurement activities in the primary grades involve using nonstandard units of measure. In this lesson, children were able to connect these prior experiences to standard units of measure. They reasoned how to use benchmarks as visual guides to 1, 10, and 20 centimeters in order to locate objects of given length ranges. They applied their earlier learning to estimate and measure the length of various objects.

Answers

Page 100
Answers will vary.

Page 101
Answers will vary. Children should indicate that they had to measure the desk in parts, then add the parts together to get the total length.

Estimating Length

Find objects in our room that fit these measurements.

1–3 Centimeters

_____   _____

_____   _____

_____   _____

_____   _____

10–15 Centimeters

_____   _____

_____   _____

_____   _____

20–25 Centimeters

_____   _____

_____   _____

_____   _____

Standard 4 Measurement

Estimating Length

**Find each object. Estimate the length.
Then measure the length.**

Object	Estimate	Actual Measurement
Pencil	_____ cm	_____ cm
Chalk	_____ cm	_____ cm
Eraser	_____ cm	_____ cm
Large paper clip	_____ cm	_____ cm
Book	_____ cm	_____ cm
Your desk	_____ cm	_____ cm

How did you measure your desk?

_____

_____

_____

_____

Estimating and Measuring Length in Inches and Feet

Introduction

Objective → Children will estimate, then measure, lengths using inches and feet.

Context → Children have had experiences measuring with a ruler and understand that 12 inches is equal to 1 foot. They will go on to do more measuring in both metric and customary units and to convert units within each system.

NCTM Standards Focus

Typically, young children have many experiences measuring length in both nonstandard and standard units. In this standards-based lesson, children use what they know about measuring to estimate the length of a variety of objects as *less than a foot, about a foot,* and *more than a foot.* Each time they estimate, they measure to check for accuracy. This allows them to gradually build their estimation skills and to develop a clear understanding of the length of a foot.

Representation Children use benchmarks to represent measurements less than 1 foot, about 1 foot, and 1 to 2 feet. They use rulers to represent more precise measurments.

Connections Children connect their previous experiences with measuring length and their understanding of benchmarks to making estimates of length in inches and feet.

Teaching Plan

Materials → student pages 106–107; chart paper; overhead projector; transparent ruler; several 1-foot objects such as an adult shoe, a 12-inch ruler, a math textbook; inch rulers

BEGIN THE LESSON by helping children find a personal referent for a foot. This will provide a basis for making reasonable estimates. In order for children to make reasonable estimates of lengths of less than 1 foot, about 1 foot, and more than a foot, they must have a general understanding of the length of a foot. *Today we're going to use estimation to decide if certain lengths are less than 1 foot, about 1 foot, and more than a foot long. What are some ways to decide whether an object is about one foot long?* (Measure it; compare it to something that you know is about a foot long.) Show children a 12-inch ruler. *Is the ruler about a foot long?* (Based on their previous measurement experiences, children should recognize that the ruler is about a foot long.) Show children other items that are about a foot long. *Are these objects also about a foot long?* Encourage children to reason that the objects are about a foot long because they are about the same length as the ruler. Point out that they do not need to actually measure the objects in order to know that they are about a foot long.

Continue the lesson by having children point out objects that are less than a foot long and more than a foot long. Ask them how they decided that the objects are longer or shorter than a foot without measuring. Encourage children to use referents other than just the ruler.

As they identify objects that are less than a foot or more than a foot, children are clarifying their ideas about how long a foot is. One of the key ideas that children should get from this lesson is that estimating without a referent is guessing. However, when they can think of an object that they know is about a foot long, they can make reasonable estimates about other lengths in relation to a foot.

CONTINUE BY WRITING three headings on a sheet of chart paper—*Less than* 1 *Foot*, *About* 1 *Foot*, and *More than* 1 *Foot*. Ask children to identify objects in the room that they think fit in each of the three categories. Record all responses.

Tell children that they are going to measure the objects listed on the chart to be sure that the objects are listed in the correct category. Measuring objects not only helps children improve their estimation and visualization skills, it gives them confidence that estimating using a referent makes sense. Place the transparent ruler on the overhead. Point out the inch markings. Beginning at 0, draw a line measuring 1 inch. While you demonstrate this, you may want to talk about the markings between inches on the ruler. Tell children that for now, they will measure to the nearest whole inch.

Choose one of the items in the *Less than* 1 *Foot* category and demonstrate how to measure it by lining it up at one end with the 0, then finding the length to the nearest inch. Again, point out that the smaller lines represent parts of an inch, but for now, children should measure to the nearest whole inch. Make sure children can identify all the inch lines—the longest numbered lines on their rulers. Have them hold up their rulers with their fingers 1 inch apart (with one finger at 0), 2 inches apart, 4 inches apart, and so on, up to 1 foot apart to reinforce the identity of the inch marks.

Model some of the problems they might run into. For example, if they do not start their measurement at the 0 mark, they will get the wrong number. If they measure in centimeters instead of inches, they will be using a different unit of measure and they won't be able to compare their results with each other.

f.y.i.

Children may not agree on how close to a foot a measurement must be to qualify for "about a foot." Discuss this with the class and establish the bounds for "about a foot"—perhaps 10–14 inches or 11–13 inches.

GROUP CHILDREN IN PAIRS. Provide them with student page 106 to use as a recording sheet, and go over the three categories on the page. Explain that the children's task is to find three different objects in the classroom that fit under each category. Challenge them to look for objects that aren't listed on the class chart. Remind them to use the benchmarks—the familiar objects discussed earlier—to help narrow their search. Observe the different approaches and strategies they use to complete the task.

Methods Children Might Use

- Children might randomly select and measure objects without any reference to the benchmarks.

- They might consistently refer to the benchmarks to select appropriate objects.

- They might find one object that fits each category, and use that object as their benchmark.

After children have recorded and measured the objects in each category, call them together. Have each pair tell about one of the objects they selected—how they chose it and how they measured it. When children share a measurement greater than 1 foot, pose these questions:

- *How did you measure the object?*
- *How did you measure objects that were longer than 12 inches?*
- *If you measured the object in parts, how did you find the total length?*
- *Would you recommend your method to others? Why or why not?*

You might wish to have children demonstrate their methods for measuring objects longer than 1 foot or have them instruct you to do so.

DISTRIBUTE STUDENT PAGE 107 for homework. Remind children to use the inch side of the ruler for these measurements. Select a few objects from the classroom and model the process of estimating and then measuring their lengths. At least two objects should be well over 2 feet long so you can demonstrate measuring to the nearest foot. Tell children to be prepared to share their findings the next day in class.

Remind children of these important measuring tips:

- Always line up one end of your object with 0 on the ruler.
- Be sure to place the straight edge of the ruler close against the object to get the most accurate measurement possible.

f.y.i.

For objects that are longer than 1 foot, you might want to talk about the units children use to record the length. For example, the same length might be recorded as either 16 inches or 1 foot 4 inches. Help children deal with these issues as they come up, but watch mainly for their ability to make a reasonable estimate and then to use and read the ruler correctly.

- If the object is longer than the ruler, measure part of the object, then mark your place and measure again. Add each section you measure to find the total length of the object.

What Might Happen . . . What to Do

Some children might return with measurements in inches that would be more appropriate in feet or vice versa. Encourage them to select the measuring unit that is the best fit for an object. Give examples such as the thickness of a dictionary or the length of the room. Would inches or feet be the appropriate unit to use? Why does it sometimes make more sense to measure in inches than feet? Feet than inches? Ask students for additional examples.

DURING YOUR REVIEW of the homework, ask children to share their results, questions, and any problems they encountered while completing the assignment. Have them share the strategies they used for one of the objects they worked with at home.

Student Pages

Student page 106 is a recording sheet for the estimating and measuring exercise in the lesson. Student page 107 asks children to first estimate, then record the actual lengths of items found at home.

Assessment

As children named objects for the class chart, you could evaluate their ability to judge a foot. While they estimated and measured lengths of objects, you could assess their estimation skills as well as their ability to use the ruler properly. You were able to check their understanding further as they shared their measurements from home.

NCTM Standards Summary

In this lesson, children connected prior measurement experiences to measuring in inches and feet. They fixed their understanding of a foot as they saw that a foot-long length can be represented by familiar objects and the foot ruler itself. Children also made connections to using benchmark measurements.

Answers

Page 106
Answers will vary.

Page 107
Answers will vary.

Estimating and Measuring Length in Inches and Feet

Complete the charts.

1 Less than 1 Foot

Object	Estimate	Length (to nearest inch)

2 About 1 Foot

Object	Estimate	Length (to nearest inch)

3 More than 1 Foot

Object	Estimate	Length (to nearest inch)

Standard 4 Measurement

Estimating and Measuring Length in Inches and Feet

1 Find two objects that are less than a foot long.
Then measure the length.

Object	Length (to nearest inch)

2 Find two objects that are more than a foot long.
Then measure the length.

Object	Length (to nearest inch)

3 Find an object that is less than 6 inches long.
Then measure the length.

Object	Length (to nearest inch)

4 Find an object that is more than 6 inches long.
Then measure the length.

Object	Length (to nearest inch)

Exploring Metric Weights

Introduction

Objective → Children will estimate the weight of objects using grams and kilograms. They will determine which objects are better measured by grams or kilograms.

Context → Children have had some experiences with the concept of weight, but this may be their initial exposure to exploring standard metric measures of weight. Children will go on to use standard measures to determine the weight of objects and to solve measurement problems involving weight.

NCTM Standards Focus

Traditionally, children are given few opportunities to physically explore the concept of weight. In this lesson, they begin to connect their experiences with weight to using a standard measure for comparing objects. They develop a point of reference for two measures (grams and kilograms) and use these to estimate the weight of various classroom objects. This hands-on, standards-based lesson provides children with a concrete experience to explore the concept of weight.

Representation Children list classroom objects as either *heavy or light*. Differences in interpretations of these headings lead children to discuss how to represent the weight of classroom objects using standard measures.

Connections Children connect their previous informal experiences with the concept of weight to more formal measurement procedures. When they are introduced to points of reference or benchmarks for a gram and a kilogram, they begin to connect the benchmarks to objects around the classroom.

Reasoning and Proof Children use reasoning and proof to determine methods of estimating the weight of objects and to devise methods for evaluating their estimates.

Teaching Plan

Materials → Student pages 112–113; pan balance; 1-kilogram weight; various classroom objects

Preparation → Fill small containers with weights or objects so that they weigh as close to 1 kilogram (2.2 pounds) as possible. You will need one for each group of four children. Also, find a hardcover book that weighs as close to 1 kilogram as possible. You will use these to demonstrate how to compare the relative weights of objects.

BEGIN THIS LESSON by asking children to find three items in the classroom that are *heavy*. Make a list of the objects on a class chart as children relay them to you. Record all responses, even if children disagree with others. Then ask children to make a list of three objects that are *light*. Again, record all responses. Once your lists are complete, ask children to look at both lists to see if they agree or disagree with what is posted. In this part of the lesson, children are making connections to their previous informal experiences with classifying objects in terms of weight. They are also using informal terms to represent the relative weights of objects.

Hold a chalkboard eraser in one hand and a hard cover book in another. *Which of these weighs more? How do you know? How could you find out?* Give a few children a chance to hold both items. As children conclude that the book definitely weighs more, introduce the terms *gram* and *kilogram*. Hold up a small paper clip and point out that it weighs *about 1 gram*. Explain that a gram is used to measure the weight of very light objects. You may want to hold up a handful of very light items (thumbtack, rubber band) to reference as objects that would be weighed in grams.

Holding the book for all to see, tell children that a kilogram is equal to the weight of 1000 grams or a little over 2 pounds. Survey the class as to whether the book weighs less than a kilogram, about a kilogram, or more than a kilogram. Post the results of this informal survey. Then ask children to suggest how you could find out how much the book actually weighs. Elicit from them that you could weigh the book on a scale.

PLACE THE PAN BALANCE in view of the children. Explain that one method for comparing the weights of objects is to use a balance like the one displayed. Place one of the small containers (1 kg) on one side of the balance. Select an object you have around the room and place it on the other end of the balance. *What happened? Did the pans balance or did one side appear lower than the other?* Talk through this process with the children, questioning them as to how the balance can be used to compare the weights of two objects.

Return to the book and ask children how else they might find out if the book weighs less than, equal to, or more than one kilogram. If the book fits on the balance, that's one way to check, but what if it's too large? Choose a child to come to the front of the room. Have him/her extend both arms with the palms up. Place a 1-kg weight in one palm and the book in the other. *Do these weigh the same or does one weigh more than the other?* Repeat the process with several children. Your preparation should pay off as children determine that the book weighs about the same as a kilogram.

Place children in groups of 2–4. Give them student page 112 to use as a recording sheet. Also provide each group with one of the small containers weighing 1 kilogram. Instruct them that their task is to find at least three different objects in the classroom that fit under the three categories. They may use some of the items on the original class chart but challenge them to look for new objects. Tell them that the 1-kilogram weight should serve as their point of reference, or benchmark, for comparing the weight of various objects.

While children work together to identify objects to record and measure, observe the different approaches and strategies they use. Children should be using reasoning and proof to determine methods of evaluating the weight of objects and then proving their methods.

AFTER CHILDREN HAVE WEIGHED at least three objects for each category, redirect their attention to the front of the room. Have them share some of the objects they recorded. For those objects that are easily moved, have children bring them to you and group them according to the weight comparisons.

- *How are the objects in each group alike? How are they different?*
- *What are some other objects in or outside the classroom that weigh about a kilogram?*
- *How did you go about selecting objects to compare? Did you do any estimation before you compared an object to your 1-kilogram weight?*
- *Why is it important to have an idea of which objects weigh about 1 kilogram?*

What are some objects around the classroom that would best be measured in grams? Brainstorm with children to create a list of ten items that would be weighed in grams. Record the ideas on the overhead or a class chart. Then tell children that they are going to estimate the weight in grams of any four objects on the list. You will find the actual weight of each object so that they may compare their estimates. Arrange children in pairs and pass out student page 113 for them to use to record their information. Encourage them to use what they know about benchmarks to help them with their estimates. Students will use their reasoning skills to connect this part of the lesson with what they have learned about using benchmarks when estimating the weights of heavy objects.

WEIGH EACH OF THE OBJECTS on the class list using the pan balance. Tell children to record the actual weights of the objects they selected as they are weighed. After weighing the objects, have children complete the writing question at the bottom of student page 113.

Close this lesson by going quickly around the room, naming an object and asking children if the object would best be weighed in grams or kilograms. Make sure that every child gets the chance to respond at least once.

Student Pages

Student page 112 provides a place for children to list classroom objects that they believe weigh less than one kilogram, about one kilogram, or more than one kilogram. Student page 113 provides children with a place to first estimate, then record the actual weight in grams of four items from a class list of items that would be weighed in grams.

Assessment

While children made their initial list of objects for the class chart, you were able to assess their interpretations of the concepts of "heavy" and "light." As they worked in groups, you observed the methods they employed to find objects that weighed less than a kilogram, about a kilogram, or more than a kilogram. You noted whether they used a 1-kilogram weight as their point of reference for comparing objects. You observed the children use information about objects that are weighed in grams to create their own benchmarks for estimating the weight of relatively light objects. You then provided them with an opportunity to share their methods for making estimates.

NCTM Standards Summary

Children actively participated in concrete experiences where they represented the weight of objects using different measures. They learned which measures are most appropriate for weighing lighter and heavier objects and immediately applied this new learning. Children made connections with prior measurement experiences by creating and utilizing benchmarks for estimating the weight of objects. They used reasoning and proof to devise methods for making and evaluating these estimates.

Answers

Page 112
Objects will vary.

Page 113
Estimates and actual weights will vary.

Exploring Metric Weights

Kilogram Hunt

Work with your group. Find at least 3 objects in the classroom that fit under each heading in the chart.

Weight of Object

Less than 1 kilogram	About 1 kilogram	More than 1 kilogram

Standard 4 Measurement

Exploring Metric Weights

Gram Hunt

Select 4 objects from the class list. Estimate the weight of each object in grams. Record the actual weight when your teacher weighs each object.

Object	Estimated Weight	Actual Weight
	grams	grams
	grams	grams
	grams	grams
	grams	grams

How did you make your estimates?

_____

_____

_____

_____

Telling Time to the Hour

Introduction

Objective → Children will tell time to the hour and relate time to daily experiences.

Context → This lesson begins a unit on time. Future lessons will include measuring time by the half hour and quarter hour.

Name _____

Telling Time to the Hour
• •

Think

Why is it important to learn to tell time?

Learn

The same time can be shown on two different clocks.

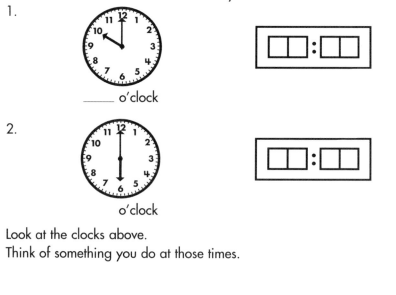

Write the time on each clock in two ways.

1.

_____ o'clock

2.

_____ o'clock

Look at the clocks above.
Think of something you do at those times.

NCTM Process Standards Analysis and Focus

The standards analysis examines how the process standards have been incorporated into the above lesson. By increasing the focus on three of the process standards, a more effective and meaningful lesson can be presented. The suggestions offered can help you to think about how this might be accomplished.

Connections Connections are loosely established as children view the same time shown on both an analog and digital clock. They are asked to think of activities that might be done at particular times without distinction as to a.m. or p.m.

Suggestion → Consider activities that make connections to other increments of time such as years, months, weeks, days, hours, minutes, and seconds.

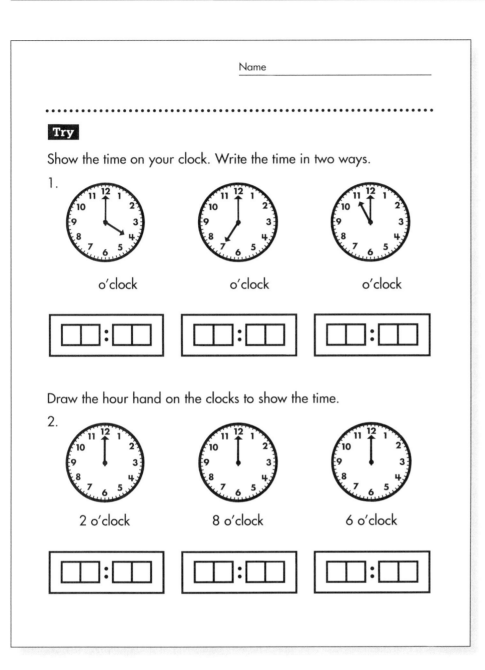

Name _____

Try

Show the time on your clock. Write the time in two ways.

1.

o'clock   o'clock   o'clock

Draw the hour hand on the clocks to show the time.

2.

2 o'clock   8 o'clock   6 o'clock

Provide background information about these units and how they relate to one another. If appropriate, include general information about how time was measured in earlier cultures. Broadening the scope of the lesson in these ways will help children to see the many facets of time and how they are interrelated.

Representation Analog and digital clock representations on lesson pages show two ways to represent time on the hour. Children are instructed to look at the two visuals and write the correct time.

Suggestion → Use an analog clock with only an hour hand to demonstrate how the hour hand serves two functions: it points directly to a number to indicate "o'clock"; it points to positions between numbers to indicate increments of time before or after the hour. Identifying

time relative to the position of the hour hand builds a strong foundation for more precise reading of time later on.

Reasoning and Proof While telling time to the hour involves reading the face of the clock, reasoning is not required.

Suggestion → Using an analog clock that has only an hour hand, position the hour hand between numbers and ask children to identify the hour just passed and the hour coming up. Ask children whether it is closer to the hour just passed or to the next hour. Encourage children to explain how they determined their answers.

Communication Except for being asked to describe things they might do at given times, children's communication is limited to written responses.

Problem Solving Because the purpose of the lesson is to recognize and identify, problem solving is not called for.

The teaching plan that follows shows how the suggestions for increasing the focus on the process standards can be implemented.

Revised Teaching Plan

Materials → Demonstration analog clock with hour and minute hands; standard analog clock; digital clock; student analog clocks; various tools for measuring time

Ways to Measure Time	
seconds	months
hours	years
minutes	decades
days	centuries
weeks	

BEGIN THE LESSON BY REVIEWING children's knowledge of time and different ways that people measure time. *How is time important to you? What are some different ways to measure time?* Guide your discussion to include "time" terms such as *seconds, minutes, hours, days, weeks, months,* and *years.* Take time to elaborate how days are grouped together to make weeks, weeks grouped to make months, months to years, and so on. Point out how days are also divided into smaller increments, for example, days are divided into hours, hours into minutes, and so on. This should not be a technical discussion, but the information helps to broaden the concept of time and puts telling time into a meaningful context.

HAVE CHILDREN COMPARE UNITS OF TIME. *Which is a longer amount of time, a second or a minute? A minute or an hour?* To help children better understand these time increments, invite them to sit quietly for a second and then for a minute with their eyes closed, opening them only when they think a minute has passed. List these terms on the board in order from smallest to greatest: *second, minute, hour.* Let children know that there are even larger units of time. For example, remind children that we are now in a new century, which marks the beginning of a period of 100 years.

What Might Happen . . . What to Do

Children may not realize that there are 24 hours in a day and that a day is divided into two parts of 12 hours each. Explain that a.m. represents morning from 12 at night to 12 noon, and p.m. represents afternoon and night from 12 noon to 12 at night. Demonstrate the importance of identifying a.m. and p.m. Would most people go to sleep at 9 a.m. or 9 p.m.? Would lunch be eaten at 12 a.m. or 12 p.m.?

Challenge children to tell what a year represents. They may suggest 365 days or 12 months. Help children to understand that a year measures the amount of time it takes the earth to revolve or travel around the sun. As the earth moves around the sun, it rotates or spins, creating periods of dark and light, which make up our days and nights. Discussing how time relates to the sun and earth not only helps to broaden the concept of time, but it also provides a way to integrate math into other areas of the curriculum.

DISPLAY A VARIETY of instruments used to measure time, such as analog and digital clocks, wristwatches, stopwatches, timers, and hourglasses. Invite children to talk about each one and to suggest others. Tell children that although many different instruments can be used, they will be dealing only with standard clock faces and digital clocks in this lesson.

Draw children's attention to the analog and digital clocks. *How are these clocks alike? How are they different?* Point out how the digital clock shows time in hours and minutes separated by a colon. *Do any of you have digital watches? Where else have you seen a digital clock?* Help children to think of objects that have digital clocks, such as VCRs, ovens, and alarm clocks.

Use an analog clock to develop conceptual understandings about time. As you describe the clock, use related terms such as *hour hand, numbers, minute hand, digital clock, analog clock, clock face,* and *clockwise.* Review the markings on the clock face as well as the functions of the two hands. *Who can tell me about the numbers that appear on the face of the clock? How many numbers do you see? What do they represent? How much time is represented when the hour hand moves from one number to the next, for example, from 1 to 2 or from 3 to 4? What about from 10 to 11? Do you know what the direction around the clock is called?* (Clockwise) Guide children to see that the distance between each consecutive pair of numbers on the clock face represents five minutes. Have children count aloud by 5s as you point to the numbers. Investigating concepts of time promotes the use of other math skills such as estimation, skip counting, and addition.

DEMONSTRATE HOW THE MINUTE HAND moves around the clock every 60 minutes, while in that same time, the hour hand moves from one number to the next. Show how on every hour, the minute hand points directly to 12 and the hour hand points directly to the number that shows the hour. Explain that the minute hand helps make it possible to tell time very precisely—to the nearest minute. Briefly discuss school or home events that take place on the hour such as lunchtime, recess, bedtime, or story time. Children's understandings are strengthened when they are able to connect ideas to everyday experiences.

Use a demonstration clock with an hour hand only. Explain that most clocks have two hands, a longer one that describes minutes, and a shorter one that describes the hours. Some clocks have three hands, the third hand counting off seconds. These hands move around the clock at different speeds. In one hour, while the minute hand makes a complete circle around the clock, the hour hand moves from one number to the next. The second hand makes a complete circle every minute. Remind children that the demonstration clock is special because it shows only the hour hand. Slowly move the hour hand to various positions on the clock. Explain that when the hour hand points directly to a number, we say it is that "o'clock."

Move the hour hand to point directly to "4." Invite a volunteer to tell the time. Explain that 4 o'clock means "four hours." Distribute student clocks for children to practice displaying times. *What time would it be if the hour hand were pointing directly to 6? To 12? To 9?* Model the activity several times to reinforce children's understanding of the skill. Consider questions to challenge and extend understandings. *How often does the hour hand point directly to a number each day? What time will it be in 2 hours? In 4 hours?*

f.y.i.

If an analog clock with only an hour hand is not available, cover the minute hand of the demonstration clock with construction paper that matches the color of the clock face. Another idea would be to tape the minute hand to the hour hand. Explain to children that this modified clock represents only the hour hand and that the minute hand will be looked at later.

Position the hour hand between two numbers on the demonstration clock. *What time is it when the hour hand is here? What o'clock or hour has just passed? What will the next o'clock or hour be?* Ask volunteers to estimate the time shown. Encourage them to use terms such as *about, almost, between __and __,* and *just before __.* Telling time when the hour hand is between numbers happens far more frequently than telling time on the hour. Learning to read the position of the hour hand lays a foundation for being able to tell time accurately in the future.

Conclude the lesson by presenting different times on the hour on a digital clock. Have children complete activities that involve transferring information from the digital clock to their analog clocks. Observe children as they move the hands on their clocks. You may also wish to challenge children by having them represent analog times digitally.

Student Pages

Children are now ready to complete exercises similar to those on the reduced student pages.

Assessment

There were opportunities to determine whether children understood telling time by the hour as they displayed time on their own clocks. Observing how children moved clock hands and documented time provided insight about their understanding. Children's responses to discussion questions provided additional insights about their understanding of telling time to the hour.

NCTM Standards Summary

There were multiple opportunities for children to make connections among increments of time such as days, hours, minutes, and seconds. Connections made to children's everyday experiences helped them internalize the usefulness of time in their lives. Students explored and compared how time is represented on analog and digital clocks. They reasoned about the position of the hour hand to determine whether it was before or after a given hour and to lay a foundation for telling time more precisely. Throughout the lesson, children were asked to question, react, and elaborate on their understandings, thus developing important critical-thinking skills.

Standard 5 **Data Analysis and Probability**

AT THE SECOND GRADE LEVEL, data analysis and probability includes a lot of work with representing and interpreting data, and probability concepts. Our lessons are derived from these important topics, and include a lesson on using Venn diagrams to represent data, a lesson in which children compare different representations of the same data, a lesson in which children determine whether a particular outcome is more likely or less likely to occur, and a lesson on performing a probability experiment and recording the data.

Three lessons model how the process standards can be used to teach content. One lesson is a hypothetical textbook lesson that we have revised to be more standards based. These four lessons do not represent the entire curriculum, but rather provide four glimpses of how, with a more concentrated effort to incorporate the process standards, better mathematics teaching and learning can be achieved.

In one lesson we have chosen, children classify objects using a Venn diagram. The process standards of problem solving, communication, and reasoning and proof are important here as this lesson focuses on sorting a collection of objects by different attributes. The Venn diagram is made on the floor, using circles. Children discuss the placement of each object within the context of the circles.

Another lesson we have chosen is one that has children examine more than one representation of the same data. Representation is an important process standard here, as are reasoning and proof and communication. Children discuss their thinking about whether different representations do show or do not show the same data.

A third lesson that we have chosen is one on probability in which children try to predict the number of cubes of each color in a bag. This lesson is driven by the process standards of reasoning and proof and communication. Children have to use the information from the random samples to determine the contents of the bag.

The hypothetical textbook lesson that we have chosen to revise has children perform a probability experiment and record the data. A typical lesson generally provides data and has the children make some record of it. Through better incorporation of the process standards of problem solving, reasoning and proof, and communication, children generate their own data and decide how to record it. Children use the data to make predictions about future outcomes.

Standard 5 Lessons

Using Venn Diagrams

Interpreting Data

Exploring Probability

Investigating Probability

Using Venn Diagrams

Introduction

Objective → Children will be able to sort and classify objects using Venn diagrams.

Context → Children have already had some experiences sorting objects by different attributes, such as color, size, and shape. They know the names of basic geometric shapes, such as square, circle, and triangle. The lesson will lead children to be able to classify data according to more complex criteria, and to organize data into like groups.

f.y.i

Consider using a different color for each ring to provide visual support in distinguishing between them. This will also facilitate identifying what is within the boundaries of a ring.

NCTM Standards Focus

Children will experience how an object can be seen in different ways to reflect the criteria being used. This skill is basic to both graphing and data analysis, where a sample can be looked at in different ways and for different purposes. Knowing how to examine information in multiple perspectives will lead students toward being intelligent consumers of data; they will better understand how to use data to make good decisions.

Reasoning and Proof Children will compare objects to identify attributes and then compare and contrast different objects. They will explain their thinking as they sort and place items into Venn diagrams.

Representation Children will determine attributes of items and will use Venn diagrams to classify the items according to attributes. They will represent classifications with manipulatives and in written form.

Communication Children will describe attribute blocks and will discuss how they should be classified. In small groups or pairs they will discuss criteria and classify blocks according to criteria they create.

Teaching Plan

Materials → Student pages 126–127; attribute blocks; yarn or hula hoops; sentence strips; chart paper; a paper bag containing a set of attribute blocks; sets of attribute blocks for groups of 2

Preparation → Prior to the lesson, prepare pairs of sentence strips to describe attributes by which to sort blocks. Pairs might include red and squares, blue and yellow, circles and triangles, and so on. Use hula hoops or string to make rings to represent Venn diagrams. Make a set of two rings that do not touch or overlap. Label these rings with prepared labels that will result in sorting blocks into distinct categories, such as triangles and squares. Make a second set of two rings that overlap. In these rings, place labels such as *red* and *square* to create overlapping attributes.

BEGIN THE LESSON by gathering children around the rings. Explain that the rings represent *Venn diagrams* and are used to sort things.

Direct attention to the pair of separate circles. Point to the label *triangles* and explain that it means only things shaped like triangles should be placed inside this ring. Point to the label *squares. What do you think this sign means?* (Only things shaped like squares should be placed inside that ring.)

Explain to children that they will take turns sorting attribute blocks by selecting one block from a bag and placing it where it belongs. Display a set of attribute blocks to review that they are of different shape, size, thickness, and color. Then place the set of blocks into a paper bag.

Invite a child to select a block from the bag, describe its attributes, and place it where it belongs in the Venn diagram. If the shape selected is a square or a triangle, the child should have no difficulty placing it. Invite other children to select, describe, and place blocks until a child selects a block that does not have the attributes being identified. At this point, additional instruction will be needed. Help children decide where shapes that are not defined should be placed. *What shapes can go inside the rings we have?* (Squares or triangles) *Is this shape a square or a triangle?* (No.) *Does it belong inside one of the rings?* (No.) Establish that shapes that do not belong inside one of the rings should be placed outside the rings, and have the child place the block in an appropriate position.

Have children continue to take turns reaching into the bag and selecting a block to place in the appropriate place inside or outside the rings. As each block is placed, have children affirm the placement and explain why the placement is correct. Continue this activity until most children can easily identify how to sort using this Venn diagram. Then have a child pick up all of the attribute blocks and place them back into the bag.

NEXT, DIRECT CHILDREN to the second Venn diagram with two overlapping rings labeled *red* and *square.* Tell children they will do another sorting activity. Point to the signs inside the rings. Establish that only red items should be placed within the boundaries of the ring labeled *red;* only square items should be placed inside the ring labeled *square.* Point out the section where the rings overlap. Explain that this section is inside the ring labeled *red* and it is also inside the ring labeled *square.* Explain that blocks that belong inside both circles will be placed there.

Clarify the directions by holding up blocks and asking questions.

- *Where does this red circle go?* (In the "red" ring where it doesn't overlap.)
- *Where should this blue square go?* (Inside the "squares" ring where it doesn't overlap.)
- *Where should this yellow triangle go?* (Outside the rings.)
- *If a red square is selected, where should it go?* (In the section where the rings overlap) Emphasize that a red square belongs inside the ring marked *red* and it also belongs inside the ring marked *squares*. Explain again that the overlapping section is inside both rings.

Place the blocks back into the bag. Have children take turns reaching into the bag, selecting a block, describing its attributes, and then placing the block in the appropriate place inside or outside the circles. As each block is placed, have children explain why the placement is correct.

When children have completed sorting the attribute blocks, reinforce the process by which placement was determined. *How did you decide which blocks were placed inside the rings?* (By the labels inside the rings.) *Which blocks went inside the overlapping section of the rings?* (Those described by both labels.) *Which blocks were placed outside of the rings?* (Those not described by the labels.) *Where were blocks that had only one of the attributes placed?* (Inside that ring but not in the overlapping sections.)

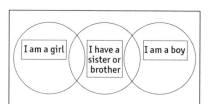

TRANSITION FROM USING MANIPULATIVES to representing Venn diagrams in written form. Draw a large rectangle on the chalkboard and inside it place three overlapping rings as shown. In one end ring write "I am a girl," in the other end ring write "I am a boy." In the center ring, write "I have a sister or brother." Then have the children write their names where they belong in the diagram. Personalizing the information being considered will help make the activity more meaningful to the children.

After everyone has written his/her name in the diagram, discuss the results. *Why aren't there any names outside the rings?* (Everyone is either a boy or a girl.) *What do we know about the names inside the center ring?* (They are boys or girls that have a sister or brother.) *Why aren't there any names in the center section of the ring labeled "I have a sister or brother?"* (That area does not include boys or girls.)

Using Venn Diagrams

Sort the letters in your name.

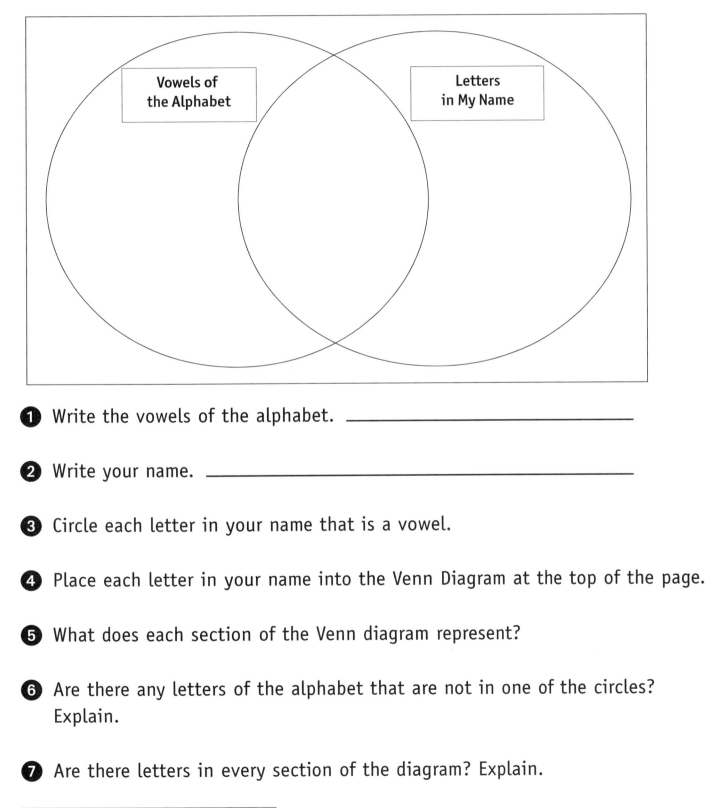

1 Write the vowels of the alphabet. _____

2 Write your name. _____

3 Circle each letter in your name that is a vowel.

4 Place each letter in your name into the Venn Diagram at the top of the page.

5 What does each section of the Venn diagram represent?

6 Are there any letters of the alphabet that are not in one of the circles? Explain.

7 Are there letters in every section of the diagram? Explain.

Interpreting Data

Introduction

Objective → Children will represent data in more than one way and describe similarities and differences between the representations.

Context → Children have collected data this year and have had experiences graphing in first grade. This is the first lesson on making graphs this year. Children will make bar graphs and focus on scale in the next lesson.

NCTM Standards Focus

In this lesson children will see that data can be shown in different ways. They will discuss how the information communicated by means of a graph is affected by the representation. They will talk about the main elements of each graph and how to create each element.

Communication Children focus on the fact that graphs have differences that affect how they communicate. Throughout this lesson, children talk in small groups or in the large class group about the data, how it is presented, and what it means.

Representation Children analyze and create multiple presentations of data.

Reasoning and Proof Children discuss the different presentations of data and reason about how the presentations are similar and how they are different.

Teaching Plan

Materials → Student pages 132–133; rectangles (about 2 inches by 4 inches) of several different colors; a simple picture of a child that can be colored and cut out for use on a pictograph; chart paper for making both a pictograph and a bar graph

IN THIS LESSON CHILDREN will be making both a pictograph and a bar graph and comparing them. Before beginning the lesson, you may wish to prepare a simple representation of a child for each child. Children will be using this figure for the pictograph. Make sure that the small rectangles that each child will use for the bar graph are the same size, and that there are enough of the same color so that each child who picks the same activity will get the same color.

Tell the children that you would like to be able to leave information for a substitute teacher or for visitors that tells them what the favorite recess activities of the class are. First tell children that you need to get the information. Discuss how to obtain the information. A sample set of data is listed below.

Soccer—8   Tag—5   Jump Rope—9   Hop Scotch—3

Tell the children that you would like to make a display to show the substitute or the visitors what the class likes. Ask for suggestions for what they could do to make the display. You may wish to include some of their suggestions as part of the lesson.

Tell them that you would like to make two types of graphs to show the information. First, you would like to make a pictograph. Ask children to tell what they know about pictographs and how they could make one. Have children discuss how they can represent children on the graph. Either give children the pictures of the children you made for them or have them make their own pictures.

NOW MAKE SURE CHILDREN UNDERSTAND all the points they need for making the pictograph; the title, the key, and the listing of the favorite activities. Talk with the children about where they need to put them on the graph, except for the key. Then put them on the chart paper. Now take some time to discuss the key. Ask children what one figure should represent. Once you decide, have the children come up and put their pictures on the correct spot on the graph. If you have a figure stand for two children, have two children come up together and put one figure on the graph, or, if necessary, have one child cut a figure in half.

Now tell children they are going to make a different type of graph called a bar graph. Tell them that a bar graph explains the same information as the pictograph but that it shows the information by the length of a bar instead of using pictures. Discuss with children what they need to put on the bar graph to make it.

Children will see that they need some of the same things. They will need a title, a list of the activities, and a scale for the side to show what the lengths of the bars mean. Decide on the title and the listing. This should be pretty similar to, if not the same as, the pictograph.

f.y.i.

Children may have different ideas of how to gather the information. Make sure that while gathering the information, each child lists and remembers his or her favorite recess activity. Later each child will be receiving pictures for the pictograph and a piece of construction paper for the bar graph that reflects their choice.

f.y.i.

You may wish to have children make their own pictures. Making the pictures could be difficult but it also has the potential to help children learn some valuable concepts. Discuss with them whether all the figures should look the same and be the same size. They need to understand that the people should at least be the same size because they do not want people to think that bigger pictures represent more people. However, coloring them differently should not affect the reading of the graph, and could communicate that each picture represents a different child.

Now tell children you are going to develop the scale for the side. Tell them that they will use their pieces of colored paper to make the bar. Help children see that the scale will need to be as high as the greatest number of children selecting an activity. Now make the side scale. Have children bring their pieces of construction paper up and construct the bar. As they do so, have children read the bar and the scale.

When you have finished the bar graph, have children look at both the bar graph and the pictograph side by side. Ask questions about the information contained in the graphs. Make sure children look at both graphs.

What Might Happen . . . What to Do

Some children might have trouble reading a bar graph that is not placed on a grid. Have them use a ruler or straightedge, putting it at the top of the bar and aligning the left edge with the scale.

Make sure children see that they can get the same information from a bar graph and a pictograph. Then ask them to tell what they like about the pictograph and what they like about the bar graph. Ask them which they think they would like to use in their room and why.

The major difference between a bar graph and a pictograph is that in the bar graph you can determine the amount the bar shows by looking at the scale and the bar. With a pictograph you will usually need to do some mental calculations to determine how many items there are. A pictograph has the potential to attract more attention because of the pictures.

Review with children how to make each graph. Show them some graph paper and discuss how they would use that to make a bar graph. You may wish to assign the student pages.

Student Pages

Student page 132 provides children with data for making a pictograph and a bar graph. They make a pictograph at the bottom of the page. Student page 133 is grid paper for children to use with the bar graph.

Assessment

You had the opportunity to assess children's understanding of pictographs and bar graphs as children discussed and made the class graphs. You had additional opportunities when children made their own graphs.

NCTM Standards Summary

In this lesson, children focused on making graphs, working with representation, and the communication of data. Children began to analyze the benefits of different data representations when they compared the two types of graphs.

Answers

Page 132
Graphs may vary.

Page 133
Graphs may vary

Interpreting Data

Make a pictograph and a bar graph using this information. Make the pictograph on the bottom of this page and the bar graph on the graph paper on the opposite page.

How We Get to School	
Car	3
Bus	8
Walk	10
Bike	2

Interpreting Data

Make your bar graph on this page.

Exploring Probability

Introduction

Objective → Children will determine which set of data is most likely produce certain results.

Context → Children are able to state outcomes for simple probability events. They can identify that tossing one number cube will produce six different possible outcomes. This lesson will serve as an underlying concrete experience for later lessons in which children will learn how to express probability in a precise way.

NCTM Standards Focus

The study of probability begins with children recognizing that some events may be more or less likely to occur than other events. They understand that some things could never happen, and are, therefore, impossible; other things are sure to happen and are, therefore, certain. They begin to look at certain data sets and random samples and conclude which samples are more likely to come from which sets. Concrete activities that the children take part in can solidify these concepts and lay the groundwork for the more precise understanding of probability that will come in later years.

Problem Solving The lesson takes a problem solving approach. Children are given a sample and challenged to decide which of several data sets the sample is most likely to come from.

Reasoning and Proof Children decide between mathematically more and less likely alternatives. They investigate what their data tells them and make a logical decision based on the data.

Teaching Plan

Materials → Student pages 138–139 (2 copies of page 138 per child); a sturdy opaque bag containing 5 cubes of one color and 5 cubes of another color; a sturdy opaque bag containing 7 cubes of one color and 3 cubes of another color (yellow and green will be referred in the lesson); cubes need to be identical in size and shape.

SHOW THE BAG containing 5 yellow and 5 green cubes to the children. Tell them there are ten cubes in the bag — some yellow cubes and some green cubes. Do not tell children how many cubes of each color are in the bag. Ask children to guess how many cubes of each color are in the bag.

Give each child two copies of student page 138 to use as a recording sheet. Tell children that they will remove one cube from the bag, record its color, and return it to the bag. They will repeat the process ten times, each time recording the result.

Ask a child to draw a cube. Record the color of the cube on chart paper or on the board and also have the class record the color on their worksheets. *Are you now certain that there was at least one [color of cube] cube in the bag?* (Yes.) *Why are you certain?* (Because we saw it.) *Do you know anything else about the cubes in the bag?* (No.) Make sure the cube is returned to the bag. Tell children that they will draw another cube. *Will the cube drawn be a different one?* (It might be.) *Might it be the same one?* (It might be.) *Why?* Make sure that children understand that each cube is as likely to be drawn as any other.

Have children continue drawing a single cube and returning it to the bag until there have been ten draws. As they draw the cubes out, continue to ask the children what they think they know about the contents of the bag. As the number of draws increases, children's ideas may change. Invite children to talk about how their ideas have changed and why. It is important that they understand that it may make sense to modify their ideas as they get more information. After ten draws have been completed, engage children in a discussion about the experiment.

Do we now know for certain what is in the bag? (No.)
We drew ten times. Why don't we? (We never saw all the cubes at the same time.)
What do you think is in the bag? Why do you think that?
If we drew a hundred times, could we be absolutely sure of the number of blocks of each color? (No.) *Why not?*

Affirm the idea that children will get a better sense of the bag's contents by drawing more times. Ask them to make a prediction about what is in the bag based on the results of the ten draws. Have them write their predictions at the bottom of their worksheets. Then show them the contents of the bag. Discuss whether or not the results were surprising and why they were or were not.

NOW TELL CHILDREN that you have another bag of ten cubes and you want them to do the same kind of experiment they did with the first bag of cubes. Show them the bag that contains 7 yellow and 3 green cubes. As before, have the children draw a single cube, record its color, and return it to the bag. Continue for ten draws asking the same kinds of questions you asked during the first experiment. Be sure to ask children how many cubes of each color they think are in the bag as the experiment is going on.

f.y.i.

Often children are disappointed or feel they are wrong if they don't guess the right number – especially if someone else guesses the right number. Help children see that their goal is to make an intelligent guess based on the information available.

When the tenth draw has been completed, ask children to make a final prediction. However, instead of showing children how many cubes of each color are in the bag, tell them that they will do another ten draws. Discuss with them whether they think drawing ten more times will help them make a better prediction.

What Might Happen . . . What to Do

Often when children are confronted with a second sample of the same data set, they totally disregard the first. For example, if the first ten draws resulted in 6 yellow and 4 green cubes, children may guess the there are 6 yellow and 4 green cubes in the bag. Then if the next ten draws resulted in 8 yellow and 2 green cubes, they will change their guess to 8 yellow and 2 green. To encourage children to think about combining the two samples, you may want to ask them how many draws were made altogether and what the results were.

CONTINUE WITH THE SECOND SAMPLE and record the results. Ask children to revise their predictions based on the total sample of twenty draws. Show the class the contents of the bag. Talk with children about how closely the sample reflects the results. Make sure you discuss the concept of adding the two samples together. *How many draws were made all together?* (20) *How many draws resulted in yellow? in green?*

Conclude the lesson having children do page 139 as a whole class activity. The page contains a situation and question designed to stimulate children's thinking about the concepts covered in the lesson.

Student Pages

Student page 138 is a recording sheet for use during the class activity. Student page 139 extends children's thinking by presenting a slightly different situation from the one encountered in the class activity, and asks children to reason about the results of a sample they did not take themselves.

Assessment

Children showed their ability to think logically about probability when they made predictions about how many cubes of each color were in the bags. Discussions held during the experiments and at their conclusions provided information about whether children understood the concept.

NCTM Standards Summary

Children engaged in experiments that laid a foundation for using a random sample to make predictions about a data set. They used their sense of number to make predictions about what a data set contained.

Answers

Page 138
This page is a chart for class use.

Page 139
The questions on the page are intended for discussion. Answers may vary.

Exploring Probability

Write the color of the cube that was drawn from the bag.

Draw	Color
1	
2	
3	
4	
5	
6	
7	
8	
9	
10	

Standard 5 Data Analysis and Probability

Exploring Probability

Answer the questions.

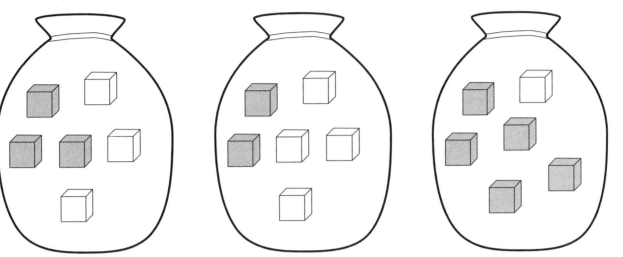

Joey and Marina have a mystery bag. They drew 30 times. Here is their tally:

☐	ⅢⅠ ⅢⅠ ⅢⅠ ‖
▨	ⅢⅠ ⅢⅠ ‖‖

1 Which of the three bags above is probably not the bag Joey and Marina have? Why do you think so?

2 Joey thinks they have the bag with 3 ▨ and 3 ☐. Marina thinks they have the bag that is 2 ▨ and 4 ☐. Do you agree with either Joey or Marina?

3 They open up the bag and find that the bag has 3 ▨ and 3 ☐. Marina thinks her guess was not a good one. Do you agree?

Steve and Ava have a bag, too. This is what their tally looks like.

4 What bag do you think Steve and Ava have? Why?

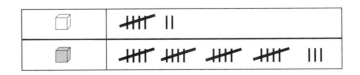

☐	ⅢⅠ ‖
▨	ⅢⅠ ⅢⅠ ⅢⅠ ⅢⅠ ‖‖

Investigating Probability

Introduction

Objective → Children will perform probability experiments and record data.

Context → This is an introductory lesson in the study of probability. Children will continue to explore the concept of probability by predicting and testing outcomes using spinners.

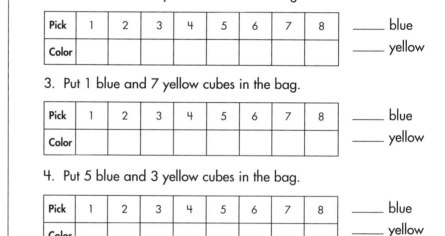

Name _____

Investigating Probability
....

Learn

1. How many times was each color picked?

Pick	1	2	3	4	5	6	7	8
Color	G	R	R	G	R	R	G	R

_____ green
_____ red

Put some blue and yellow cubes in a bag.
Pick one cube and color the chart to show your pick.
Put the cube back. Pick 8 times.
Write the number of times you picked each color.

2. Put 4 blue and 4 yellow cubes in the bag.

Pick	1	2	3	4	5	6	7	8
Color								

_____ blue
_____ yellow

3. Put 1 blue and 7 yellow cubes in the bag.

Pick	1	2	3	4	5	6	7	8
Color								

_____ blue
_____ yellow

4. Put 5 blue and 3 yellow cubes in the bag.

Pick	1	2	3	4	5	6	7	8
Color								

_____ blue
_____ yellow

NCTM Process Standards Analysis and Focus

The standards analysis examines how the process standards have been incorporated into the above lesson. By increasing the focus on three of the process standards, a more effective and meaningful lesson can be presented. The suggestions offered can help you to think about how this might be accomplished.

Problem Solving The lesson involves recording information but does not present any problem-solving situations.

Suggestion → Introduce problem solving into the lesson by having children pick counters from bags without being given information about the bag's contents. Use an inquiry-oriented approach to encourage children to think about the number and color of the counters the

Name _____

• •

Try

Guess the number of times you will pick each color.
Write your guess.
Pick a cube 10 times. Color the chart to show your pick.
Write the number of times you picked each color.

1. Put 2 blue and 8 yellow cubes in the bag.

Pick	1	2	3	4	5	6	7	8	9	10
Color										

Guess: blue _____ yellow _____ **Actual:** blue _____ yellow_____

2. Put 0 blue and 10 yellow cubes in the bag.

Pick	1	2	3	4	5	6	7	8	9	10
Color										

Guess: blue _____ yellow _____ **Actual:** blue _____ yellow_____

3. Put 4 blue and 6 yellow cubes in the bag.

Pick	1	2	3	4	5	6	7	8	9	10
Color										

Guess: blue _____ yellow _____ **Actual:** blue _____ yellow_____

4. Kayla has 10 colored cubes in a bag. Some
are red and some are yellow. She picked a
cube 10 times. She picked yellow 4 times and
red 6 times.
Predict how many cubes of each color are in   _____ red
the bag.   _____ yellow

bag might contain. Then have them examine the data compiled during the activity to figure out the configuration of the bag's contents.

Reasoning and Proof Children are asked to place a given number of each color counter into a bag. Then they are instructed to tell the color they picked most often and offer an explanation.

Suggestion → Invite children to examine data compiled on their selections and make conjectures about the contents of the bag. Encourage them to look for patterns or trends. Check children's speculations by showing the contents of each bag. Work with children to predict outcomes for selections and compare their predictions to the actual results.

Activities such as these will heighten children's awareness of judging results as well as making predictions.

Communication Children guess how many times they will pick a certain color but have little opportunity to discuss the reasonableness of their guesses.

Suggestion → During children's investigations, model the language of probability to help them develop both an understanding of the mathematical concept and an awareness of terms. Discuss outcomes and predictions in light of data. This will help dispel erroneous thinking about what might happen.

Connections Teacher notes suggest presenting two choices of what might occur in a given situation and predicting the likelihood of having one or the other happen.

Representation The lesson uses counters in an assortment of colors to represent possible choices. Completed charts document children's results as they pick counters from a bag.

The teaching plan that follows shows how the suggestions for increasing the focus on the process standards can be implemented.

Revised Teaching Plan

Materials → Three paper bags; a combination of 2 colors of counters (or square tiles) for each bag

BEFORE THE LESSON, prepare three bags by filling them with counters as indicated and labeling them A, B, and C:

- Bag A: 2 red and 8 yellow counters
- Bag B: 5 red and 5 yellow counters
- Bag C: 10 red counters

Begin the lesson with a brief explanation of probability. If possible, use real-world situations that children can relate to such as predicting weather, winning tic-tac-toe games, or possible food selections for lunch. Discuss the concept in terms of events and which is more likely to happen. *What are the chances that we will have pizza for lunch? Is it likely to rain today? Why or why not?* Throughout the lesson, children will examine and discuss choices that are more likely to happen and why. Explain that though there are often many possible choices, today's lesson will investigate only those situations having two possibilities from which to choose.

Display bag A. *There are a number of counters in this bag. How can we find out the colors of the counters and how many counters there are of each color without looking inside the bag?* Brainstorm possible ideas. Then have volunteers take turns selecting a counter from the bag without looking inside. Have children show the color of the counter to the class and then place it back in the bag. Record each pick with a tally mark on the board.

	Tally Marks	Total
red	✝✝✝ I	6
yellow	✝✝✝ III	9

After the first child has picked, ask children if they have enough information to determine the color(s) of the counters in the bag. Repeat the same

f.y.i.

Consider identifying a classroom helper to make the selection process move more smoothly. Have the helper carry the bag around the room from one child to the next. Make sure the helper holds the bag up high to prevent children from looking into it. Don't forget to have the helper select a counter from the bag.

inquiry after five children have picked, and then again after ten. Have children explain their thinking. After everyone has had a chance to pick a counter, draw children's attention to the data on the board. *Based on the information we have, what color(s) do you think the counters might be? Why? Is it likely that there was another color in the bag that no one picked? Explain your thinking.* Point out to children that while it is possible for a third color to be in the bag, it is not very likely if another color hasn't come up by the time everyone has had a turn. *How many times was a red marker picked? How many times was a yellow marker picked? Do you think there are more red or yellow counters in the bag?* Asking thought-provoking questions helps children realize the importance of critical thinking and promotes inquiry.

INVITE VOLUNTEERS TO PREDICT the color of the counters in the bag. Remind children that there are 10 counters in the bag. With this information in mind, ask children to examine the data to determine the possible color configurations of the counters. *If there are 10 counters in the bag, how many could be red and how many could be yellow?* Elicit and list the nine possible combinations. As children suggest possible combinations, have them verify that the numbers add up to 10. Record the data in an order that demonstrates a strategy to keep track of all possibilities. Data offered should range from 1 red and 9 yellow to 9 red and 1 yellow. *Should we include 0 red with 10 yellow, and 10 red with 0 yellow? Why?*

Point to each color combination and have children put thumbs up to vote for the color combination they think is in the bag. Allow time for children to explain their thinking. After all combinations have been considered, encourage children to take a few moments to reconsider their votes based on information learned during discussion. Revise the information on the board to reflect any changes of opinion.

Have a volunteer empty the bag to display the counters. Work with children to compare their predictions with the actual assortment of colors. These experiences encourage children to think through situations and to evaluate their responses based on given information.

Repeat the sequence of activities and questions with bag B and then with bag C. Continue to ask children if it's possible that a color not selected might be in one of the bags. Allow time to discuss why or why not.

f.y.i.

If the counters are not placed back in the bag after each pick, the ratio of red to yellow changes depending on the color removed, and the probability of picking either color changes accordingly. By replacing the counter after each pick, the ratio and the probability remain the same for each pick.

NOW, DIVIDE THE CLASS INTO THREE GROUPS for an experiment. Use bag B and remind children that there are 5 red and 5 yellow counters in the bag. Tell them that they will each have a chance to predict whether they will pick a red or yellow counter from the bag and they should explain their predictions. Do not comment on their reasons. Indicating that responses are correct or incorrect might discourage children from sharing their thoughts in this activity designed to introduce making predictions.

Work with one group at a time. Instruct children to reach into the bag without looking, take out a counter, hold it up for everyone to see, and then return it to the bag. Record the color. Create a separate chart for each group's results. Total the number of red and yellow counters for each group and for all three groups. *What patterns do you notice? What do you notice about the results for group 1? group 2? group 3? What about the results for all three groups? Did anything surprise you?* As children compare the charts, they will notice that the results for each group may vary, but the total will likely be closer to the equal distribution. Explain that if there were a very large number of picks, the number of reds and yellows would be closer to the same.

As children compare the charts, they will notice that the results for each group may vary but the total will probably be closer to the equal distribution. Explain that if there were a very large number of picks, the number of reds picked would most likely be about the same as the number of yellows.

Finally, discuss reasons for children's predictions. Some may have predicted red because they like that color. Others may have thought that if they concentrated very hard they'd be able to "will" their color. Explain that since there are an equal number of red and yellow counters, the chances are the same that either color will be picked. Make a connection to having just two counters, one of each color; either one or the other will be picked, and each color has an equal chance. A child might have predicted yellow after several red counters in a row were selected thinking it was yellow's turn. Explain that each time someone picks a counter, it's just as likely a red will be picked as a yellow. Remind children that the color picked is a matter of chance; there is no way to determine the color in advance. Thoughtful conversations help children to consider other points of view as they listen and discuss the reasons for their predictions.

All Group Totals

	Group 1	Group 2	Group 3
red	5	4	6
yellow	5	6	4

CONCLUDE THE LESSON by asking children to raise their hands to indicate responses as you present situations. Briefly discuss their reasons. Encourage children to use terms such as *likely*, *unlikely*, and *impossible*.

Situation A: A group of children have a box filled with counters. Each child reaches into the box to pick one and then replaces it. Here are the results: 25 blue, 5 red. *Who thinks there are more red counters in the box? more blue? an equal number of red and blue?*

Situation B: Same scenario as situation A. Here are the results: 30 green, 0 blue. *Are there more green? more blue? an equal number?*

Situation C: Same scenario as situation A. Here are the results: 12 yellow, 18 green. *Are there more yellow? more green? an equal number?*

Student Pages

Children are now ready to complete exercises similar to those on the reduced student pages. Encourage children to consider the number of each color counter and predict what they will pick before doing each experiment.

Assessment

Opportunities for assessment occurred as children predicted the configurations of each bag's contents. As children explained their thinking for possible outcomes, their level of understanding could be evaluated. When children explained their predictions, there were opportunities to assess their understanding of how likely something is to happen.

NCTM Standards Summary

An inquiry-oriented approach offered children an increased level of involvement and understanding as they solved problems of chance. Discussions enhanced children's ability to communicate mathematically and use higher-level thinking processes. Inferences about collected data were encouraged, shared, and questioned by classmates as each child elaborated on or defended his/her thinking. Meaning for probability was greatly enhanced as children discussed real-world situations and explored possible outcomes for each activity. Through discussions, children clarified and refined their understanding of likely events.

Create Your Own Lesson

THIS LAST CHAPTER IS DESIGNED TO HELP you develop your own lessons in which you can comfortably incorporate the NCTM standards with your teaching style. We start with a list of questions to help you focus on factors to consider as you begin to organize a standards-based lesson. Then we model the process used to create a lesson as you are walked through the thoughts and decisions one person used in developing a lesson.

The questions listed here are meant as a guide, a starting point; they are offered to get you thinking about how to develop your lesson, what material to cover, what steps to follow, what questions to ask. Hopefully, these questions will trigger additional ideas that you will add as you go along.

Write down the ideas that come to you as you read each question. There may be questions for which you don't have an immediate response, but don't worry; as you begin working on your lesson, ideas will come. Start by selecting the general content area. Think about the concept you want to develop. Then, narrow in on an objective for the lesson. Be specific and be realistic. What does meeting that objective mean? Is there a skill that students should be able to perform after completing the lesson? Are there questions they should be able to answer? How will you determine that the objective has been met?

Next, think about the process standards: Problem Solving, Reasoning and Proof, Communication, Connections, and Representation. What approach will be effective in helping students understand the concept? Try to envision how the lesson will flow, how it should begin, what activities and questions will be included, and how you will assess learning. Understand that there can be several ways to successfully teach any lesson. As you begin to design your lesson, new ideas will come and you will be able to refine your thinking.

Focusing Questions

1. What content standard is to be addressed? What concept within that standard is to be developed?

2. What information do the standards offer about this content?

3. What do students know about this content? What don't they know?

4. What is the specific objective of the lesson? What should students be able to do at the end of the lesson?

recognize	identify	define
review	compute	classify
compare	create	other

5. What kinds of questions should students be able to answer when they complete this lesson? What skill(s) should they be able to demonstrate?

6. What resources are available to develop this concept?

references	textual material
manipulatives	supplementary material
colleagues	student knowledge

7. What can realistically be accomplished in the time allowed?

8. Which activities and process standards can best help develop the key ideas?
   - using drawings, charts, diagrams (Representation)
   - focusing on symbols (Representation)
   - conducting small-group/large-group discussion (Communication)
   - having students gather and analyze data (Problem Solving)
   - thinking through relationships and explaining them (Reasoning and Proof and Communication)
   - finding ways to prove thinking and verify solutions (Reasoning and Proof)
   - extending/building on former knowledge (Connections)
   - integrating the concept with another discipline (Connections)
   - relating math to its use in the real world (Connections)

9. What questions will focus students' thinking on the concept and help guide learning?

Developing the Lesson

I WANT TO DEVELOP A LESSON that introduces children to two-digit addition. This lesson will be the beginning of a series of lessons in which children develop and learn a process, or the algorithm, for adding two-digit numbers. I am concerned about how this concept is often presented to children. Many of them in first grade are given two-digit addition problems without regrouping. They are told to just add the columns. This leads to multi-digit addition being taught in stages. First children add without regrouping. Then they regroup one time and then two. I think this method makes it very difficult for children to understand the concept of multi-digit addition because just as they begin to think they understand it, a new case is put in front of them. I believe we make it more difficult to learn this concept, because of the way we present it.

I want to change that approach as the standards suggest, and have children understand the big picture first, and then, use this big picture to see how to add under any conditions. Also, as the standards suggest, I want my children involved in developing their own processes. I want them to look at each other's processes and learn from them.

Before I teach this lesson, there are some things that my children need to know. Too often I have tried to push my children to learn the algorithm before they had acquired the skills they needed to be successful. They need to have good number-sense knowledge of the addition facts. For example, I want them to know which numbers make ten. They need to have a good foundation of the facts. However, I am not concerned with quickness at this point. I know that their speed and facility with the facts will improve since they will be getting a lot more practice as we do the work with multi-digit addition.

I want my children to have done some work with two-digit plus one-digit problems such as:

$$37 + 4$$

I want them to have solved these using number sense, such as counting on, rather than using an algorithm. If they have done problems like this, they will have a glimpse into the concept of two-digit addition.

Also, my children need to have lots of experiences making different numbers and seeing that the same number can be made in different ways. This means that they will also need to have worked with expanded and regular notation. For example, I want them to have looked at a problem such as:

Write this number in standard form.

2 tens and 15 ones is the same as _____.

I want may children to have done this with manipulatives and be fluent in renaming numbers different ways.

To accomplish my goals, I can see that the process standards will pay a big role. Representation will be essential. Children will need to develop their own methods and to do that, it will be essential that they represent the numbers with manipulatives. Also, it will be important that children record what they do. This recording will help them in two ways. First, it will help them think about and remember what they did. This is important because children will need to discuss each other's methods and ideas. Also, recording will lead them to their own algorithm and will eventually help them understand the standard algorithm and how it works.

Reasoning and proof will play a major role in a lesson like this. Children will have to develop a method that works. In developing this method, by using manipulatives and making records, they will have to think and reason. They will have to explain their methods to other children and defend or modify them as needed.

I have already mentioned a great deal about communication, so it is natural in this lesson. There is obvious communication as children talk about their methods. However there is another aspect of communication which may be even more important, in fact it may be the cornerstone of children's developing a process. This is the recording of their work. This involves children communicating with themselves and leaving a record so they can go back and see what they have done. Ultimately, this record can help them to develop a process they can use again and again in all situations involving multi-digit addition. This record will also be their link to the standard algorithm.

There is one more thing I need to think about before I actually start writing the lesson. I know I will need to use manipulatives, but which ones? Most of the time I don't have the luxury of deciding which manipulative to use, but for this lesson, I want to look at the different alternatives. I want to use a material that can make both tens and ones. There are two that come to mind—base-ten blocks and linking cubes. The good thing about base-ten blocks is that the tens are already made and I have enough of them. The weakness is that children will have to exchange 10 ones for 1 ten. They cannot turn the 10 ones into 1 ten on the spot. This trading may make things a little more difficult. I want children to focus on the process they are using and their recording.

With the linking cubes, on the other hand, children can join 10 ones together and make 1 ten out of the same cubes. I think this is conceptually better because children will see the ones that make up the ten. The problem with using the linking cubes is that I may not have enough of them.

I think either manipulative will work. I will use the linking cubes since I have a choice. If I had to use the base-ten blocks I would make sure to take a lot of time prior to the lesson to have children trade back and forth between tens and ones.

To start my lesson, I want to present to my children three problems in a very simple context. I am using the context to help them think about addition. I do not, however, want the context to take over the lesson. I want my children to focus on adding. The context will help me state the problems without having to write the numbers down in any particular format. I can just write the information on the board. The problems are:

1. There are 45 people in a room. Then 27 more people come into the room. How many people are there in the room now?

2. I had 32 cents and found 25 cents. How much do I have now?

3. There are 48 cubes in the box. Someone put 42 more cubes in the box. How many cubes are in the box now?

I will put children in pairs and tell them to use cubes to solve the problems. I also want them to record what they do, so they can tell other children about their methods. I will walk around the room and observe. One of my main goals will be to make sure that children are keeping records of what they do. As I said earlier, it is vital that they do. What I want to happen in later lessons, is that children's record-keeping will become their process. I will also ask them to tell me why they are doing something the way they are. For example, if they put the ones cubes together first, I will ask them why. If they start with the tens first, I will ask them why. I want them to always think about why they are doing something. I used to ask my children why they were doing something only when I thought they were doing something incorrectly. They got the cue, and the minute I asked *why* they said, "I don't think this is right."

When the groups have solved the problems, we will come back together as a class. When I call on a group to show what they did, I don't want to see just the answer. I will ask children what they did, why they did it that way, and what their records look like.

I will ask the groups to put their records on the board and explain what they did. This way we can start to link their processes to a paper and pencil algorithm. When a group has finished explaining what they did, I will ask other children to re-explain that groups work using their records. I will ask children to comment on the similarities and differences among the various methods and records. For example, some children may add the tens together first and then the ones blocks; others may add the ones first. That is fine, but I don't want to let it go at that. I want children to discuss the differences between the methods. For example, in problems 1 and 3, children who add the tens first will have to readjust the number of tens after they add the ones. I don't want to say any method is superior, I want children to understand the differences. Later, when I show them the standard algorithm they will better understand why that method starts with the ones. Next, I will give children about five more problems to solve, making sure I mix both problems that need regrouping with those that don't.

Reviewing the Plan

As I look back upon this lesson, I see it is both simple and complex. The structure of the lesson is simple—give the children three problems, have them solve and record, and then share their work. But the lesson is also complex. The decisions I have made are crucial to having my children look at the whole process of multi-digit addition and then build understanding. I believe this process will be more difficult in the beginning, but will be much more satisfying in the end.